SCHOLASTIC

BETWEEN GRADES 4&5

# SUMMER EXPRESS



NEW YORK • TORONTO • LONDON • AUCKLAND
SYDNEY • NEW DELHI • HONG KONG

Cover design by Brian LaRossa
Cover photo © Mike Powell/Gettyimages
Interior illustrations by Robert Alley, Abbey Carter, Maxie Chambliss, Sue Dennen, Shelley Dieterichs, Jane Dippold, Julie Durrell, Rusty Fletcher, James Hale, Mike Moran, Sherry Neidigh, Cary Pillo, Carol Tiernon, and Lynn Vineyard

ISBN-13 978-93-5103-916-7


Reprinted: Dec. 2016

Printed at Aegean Offset Printers, Greater Noida (U.P.)

# Table of Contents

## Dear Parent:

Congratulations! You hold in your hands an exceptional educational tool that will give your child a head start into the coming school year.

Inside this book, you'll find 100 practice pages that will help your child review and learn math, reading, writing, grammar, vocabulary, and so much more! The workbook is divided into 10 weeks, with two practice pages for each day of the week, Monday to Friday. However, feel free to use the pages in any order that your child would like. Here are other features you'll find inside:

- A weekly **incentive chart** and **certificate** to motivate and reward your child for his or her efforts.
- A sheet of **colourful stickers**. There are small stickers to reward your child for each day's work as well as a large sticker for completing the activities each week.
- Suggestions for fun, creative **learning activities** you can do with your child each week.
- A **recommended reading list** of age-appropriate books that you and your child can read throughout the summer.
- A **certificate of completion** to celebrate your child's accomplishments.
- The **answers** for all exercises in this book are available as a **downloadable PDF** on **www.scholastic.co.in**

We hope you and your child will have a lot of fun as you work together to complete this workbook.

Enjoy!
**The Editors**

# Terrific Tips for Using This Book

**1** Pick a good time for your child to work on the activities. You may want to do it around mid-morning or early afternoon when your child is not too tired.

**2** Make sure your child has all the supplies he or she needs, such as pencils and markers. Set aside a special place for your child to work.

**3** At the beginning of each week, discuss with your child how many minutes a day he or she would like to read. Write the goal at the top of the incentive chart for the week. (We recommend that a child entering fifth grade read at least 30 minutes a day.)

**4** Reward your child's efforts with the small stickers at the end of each day. As an added bonus, let your child affix a large sticker at the bottom of the incentive chart for completing the activities each week.

**5** Encourage your child to complete the worksheet, but don't force the issue. While you may want to ensure that your child succeeds, it's also important that your child maintain a positive and relaxed attitude toward school and learning.

**6** After you've given your child a few minutes to look over the practice pages he or she will be working on, ask your child to tell you his or her plan of action: "Tell me about what we're doing on these pages." Hearing the explanation aloud can provide you with insights into your child's thinking processes. Can he or she complete the work independently? With guidance? If your child needs support from a family member, try offering choices regarding with whom he or she will be working. Providing choices is an approach that can help boost your child's confidence and help him or her feel more ownership of the work to be done.

**7** When your child has finished the workbook, present him or her with the certificate of completion on page 143. Feel free to frame or laminate the certificate and display it on the wall for everyone to see. Your child will be so proud!

# Skill-Building Activities for Any Time

The following activities are designed to complement the ten weeks of practice pages in this book. These activities don't take more than a few minutes to complete and are just a handful of ways in which you can enrich and enliven your child's learning. Use the activities to take advantage of the time you might ordinarily disregard—for example, standing in line or waiting at a bus stop. You'll be working to practice key skills and have fun together at the same time.

## Finding Real-Life Connections

One of the reasons for schooling is to help children function out in the real world, to empower them with the abilities they'll truly need. So why not put those developing skills into action by enlisting your child's help with reading a map, following a recipe, checking grocery receipts, and so on. He or she can apply reading, writing, science, and math skills in important and practical ways, connecting what he or she is learning with everyday tasks.

## An Eye for Patterns

A red-brick sidewalk, a beaded necklace, a Sunday newspaper—all show evidence of structure and organisation. You can help your child recognise something's structure or organisation by observing and talking about patterns they see. Your child will apply his or her developing ability to spot patterns across all school subject areas, including alphabet letter formation (writing), attributes of shapes and solids (geometry), and characteristics of narrative stories (reading). Being able to notice patterns is a skill shared by effective readers and writers, scientists, and mathematicians.

## Journals as Learning Tools

Most of us associate journal writing with reading comprehension, but having your child keep a journal can help you keep up with his or her developing skills in other academic areas as well—from adding fractions to combining sentences. To get started, provide your child with several sheets of paper, folded in half, and stapled together. Explain that he or she will be writing and/or drawing in the journal to complement the practice pages completed each week. The journal is another tool you both can use to monitor progress of skills newly learned or practiced, or those that need improvement. Before moving on to another set of practice pages, take a few minutes to read and discuss that week's journal entries together.

## Promote Reading at Home

- Let your child catch you in the act of reading for pleasure, whether you like reading science fiction novels or do-it-yourself magazines. Store them someplace that encourages you to read in front of your child and **demonstrate that reading is an activity you enjoy**. For example, locate your reading materials on the coffee table instead of your nightstand.
- Set aside a family reading time. By designating a reading time each week, your family is assured an opportunity to discuss with each other what you're reading. You can, for example, share a funny quote from an article. Or your child can tell you his or her favourite part of a story. The key is to **make a family tradition of reading and sharing books** of all kinds together.
- **Put together collections of reading materials** your child can access easily. Gather them in baskets or bins that you can place in the family room, the car, and your child's bedroom. You can refresh your child's library by borrowing materials from your community's library, buying used books, or swapping books and magazines with friends and neighbors.

# Skills Review and Practice

Educators have established learning standards for math and language arts. Listed below are some of the important skills covered in *Summer Express* that will help your child review and prepare for the coming school year so that he or she is better prepared to meet these learning standards.

## Math

### Skills Your Child Will Review

- adding without regrouping multiplication facts
- finding area and perimeter (feet, yards)
- reading tables, charts, and bar graphs

### Skills Your Child Will Practice to Prepare for Grade Five

- solving word problems using knowledge of money values and decimals
- solving word problems using multiplication skills
- identifying equivalent fractions
- adding with regrouping
- adding decimals (e.g., money values)
- subtracting with regrouping and multiple regrouping
- subtracting fractions
- multiplying with regrouping
- multiplying decimals and whole numbers
- dividing with remainders and decimals
- changing decimals to fractions
- plotting coordinates on a grid
- matching geometric terms with corresponding shapes
- recognising equivalent decimals, fractions, and percents

## Language Arts

### Skills Your Child Will Review

- proofreading (e.g., grammar, meaning, spelling, sentence variety)
- prewriting strategies to relate information (e.g., graphic organisers)
- writing for a purpose (e.g., expository paragraph, persuasive paragraph, descriptive paragraph)
- expanding and combining sentences
- identifying topic sentences
- writing in paragraph form
- using parts of speech
- writing in upper- and lowercase cursive letters
- demonstrating knowledge of level-appropriate reading vocabulary (e.g., synonyms, antonyms, and so on)

### Skills Your Child Will Practice to Prepare for Grade Five

- using proofreading symbols (e.g., capitalisation, missing words)
- using a graphic organiser to write a concrete poem
- writing for a purpose (e.g., comparison paragraph)
- identifying incomplete sentences
- fixing run-on sentences
- adding details to increase a reader's interest
- using exact verbs to clarify meaning
- identifying parts of a paragraph
- identifying parts of speech (e.g., present-, past-, and future-tense verbs)
- using subject-verb agreement
- punctuating using commas and colons
- using supporting details
- summarising information
- using phonetic, structural, and context analysis (e.g., syllables) to identify unfamiliar words

# Helping Your Child Get Ready: Week 1

These are the skills your child will be working on this week.

**Math**

- adding without regrouping
- adding with regrouping

**Reading**

- sequencing

**Writing**

- including details

**Vocabulary**

- synonyms and antonyms
- idioms

**Grammar**

- sentence types

**Handwriting**

- uppercase cursive letters

**Here are some activities you and your child might enjoy.**

**Restaurant Review** Next time you eat out, have your child write a review of the restaurant. Encourage him or her to use lots of descriptive words.

**Secret Messages** Suggest that your child come up with a code to write secret messages in. Have him or her trade messages with you or another family member.

**Word Problem Reversals** To help your child understand tricky word problems, have him or her work in reverse! Supply a number sentence such as $5 \times 8 = 40$ or $40 \div 5 = 8$ and have your child come up with a word problem for it.

**Set a Summer's End Goal** Suggest that your child set a goal for the end of the summer. Perhaps it's becoming an expert on a favourite animal, or learning how to count in another language. Help your child come up with a plan for success.

**Your child might enjoy reading the following books:**

*Book Uncle and Me*
*by Uma Krishnaswami*

*Amber Brown and the Purple Crayon*
*by Paula Danziger*

*The Wonderful Wizard of Oz*
*by Frank Baum*

Special Note: The activity for Day 5 of this week is a mini-book. Have your child tear out the page along the perforation and cut along the dotted line. After positioning the two sections so the mini-book pages are in sequence, your child can staple and fold to form a book. Then he or she can answer all the puzzles in the mini-book.

______________________'s Incentive Chart: Week 1

Name Here

This week, I plan to read __________ minutes each day.

CHART YOUR PROGRESS HERE.

| Week 1 | Day 1 | Day 2 | Day 3 | Day 4 | Day 5 |
|---|---|---|---|---|---|
|  I read for... | minutes | minutes | minutes | minutes | minutes |
| Put a sticker to show you completed each day's work. | | | | | |

# Congratulations!

Wow! You did a great job this week!

Place sticker here.

Parent or Caregiver's Signature ______________________

# Two Left Feet

These shoes are all mixed up! You can pair them off. Each shoe contains a word that is a synonym for a word on another shoe. Synonyms are words that have the same or almost the same meaning. Put each pair of shoes together by colouring them the same colour. Use a different colour for each pair.

Lace up those synonym shoes! Each of the shoelaces has a word that is an antonym for a pair of shoes above. Antonyms are words that have the opposite meanings. Colour each lace the same colour as the pair of shoes that is its opposite.

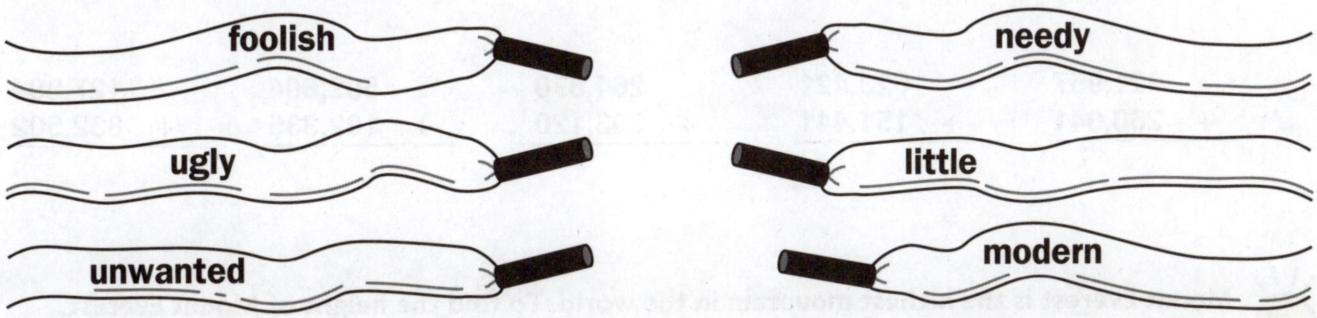


**Bonus:** Create antonym *socks*. Challenge a friend to match them to the shoes.

Week 1 • Day 1

Addition

# Climbing High

*To add multiple-digit numbers without regrouping, follow these steps.*

*1. Add the ones column.*

*2. Add the 10s column.*

*3. Add the 100s column.*

*4. Continue working through each column in order.*

Add.

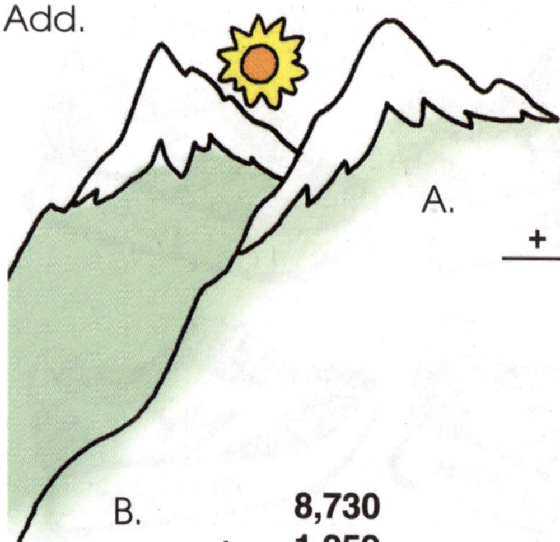

A. 1,136 + 2,433    9,025 + 851

B. 8,730 + 1,252    2,928 + 5,021    3,650 + 4,210    80,662 + 11,136

C. 55,100 + 31,892    60,439 + 30,310    81,763 + 8,231    36,034 + 41,753

D. 321,957 + 260,041    623,421 + 151,441    264,870 + 303,120    592,604 + 102,335    127,094 + 832,502

**Mount Everest is the highest mountain in the world. To find the height of Mount Everest, begin climbing in Row D. Write the underlined numbers in order. Continue writing the numbers in Row C, Row B, and Row A. How many feet did you climb?**

# Spout Some Specifics

*To be a good writer, it is important to know what you are writing about, to be specific, and to include details. All this helps to create a picture for your readers and will make your writing more interesting and informative. Compare the two phrases below. Which one is more specific, interesting, and informative? Which one creates a more vivid picture?*

*a vehicle* or *an old, rusty, dilapidated pick-up truck with flat tires and a shattered windshield*

For each general word or phrase, write a more specific word. Then add details to describe each specific word.

| | Specific Word | Details |
|---|---|---|
| 1. **a body of water** | ________ | ________ |
| 2. **a piece of furniture** | ________ | ________ |
| 3. **an article of clothing** | ________ | ________ |
| 4. **a child's toy** | ________ | ________ |
| 5. **a noise or sound** | ________ | ________ |
| 6. **a tool** | ________ | ________ |
| 7. **a group of people** | ________ | ________ |
| 8. **a reptile** | ________ | ________ |
| 9. **garden plants** | ________ | ________ |
| 10. **a kind of fruit** | ________ | ________ |
| 11. **a kind of vegetable** | ________ | ________ |
| 12. **a drink** | ________ | ________ |
| 13. **footwear** | ________ | ________ |
| 14. **musical instrument** | ________ | ________ |
| 15. **a holiday** | ________ | ________ |

**Look at yourself in the mirror. Then write on a sheet of paper as many words and phrases as you can to describe yourself so that someone who does not know you would get a clear, vivid picture of what you look like.**

# Types of Sentences

A **declarative sentence** makes a statement. An **interrogative sentence** asks a question. An **exclamatory sentence** shows strong feeling. An **imperative sentence** states a command.

A. **What kind of sentence is each of the following? Write *declarative, interrogative, exclamatory,* or *imperative* on the line.**

1. Merlin carried the baby to safety. ____________________
2. Why did traitors poison the town's wells? ____________________
3. Go back and fetch the missing sword. ____________________
4. Slip the sword into the groove, and pull it out. ____________________
5. The king was England's bravest ruler! ____________________
6. Who will follow Selene? ____________________

B. **Identify which groups of words are incomplete sentences and which are complete sentences. Write *incomplete* or *complete* on the line.**

1. Sarah at the edge of the square. ____________________
2. The knights fought so bravely! ____________________
3. How did Kay treat her dog? ____________________
4. The sword out of the stone. ____________________
5. Natalie was trained to be a pilot. ____________________

C. **Correct the incomplete sentences in part B. Add an action word to each one. Then rewrite the complete sentence on the line.**

1. ________________________________________________

2. ________________________________________________

# A Real Cool Cowboy

*The events in a story take place in a certain order. This is the* ***sequence*** *of events.*

Pecos Bill is a well-known character in American folklore. His legend developed from a magazine article written by Edward O'Reilly in 1923. This cowboy hero is often credited for being the creator of branding, roping, and other cowboy activities. It is also said that Pecos Bill taught broncos how to buck and cowboys how to ride.

Legend has it that Pecos Bill was born in the 1830s in Texas. He teethed on a bowie knife and had bears and other wild animals as friends. On a family trip to the West, little Bill fell out of the wagon near the Pecos River. He was found by coyotes that raised him.

Two famous natural landmarks are also amusingly traced back to Pecos Bill—the Grand Canyon and Death Valley. Supposedly, Pecos Bill once made a bet that he could ride an Oklahoma cyclone without a saddle. The cyclone was not able to throw him off, and it finally "rained out" under him in Arizona. This rain was so heavy that it created the Grand Canyon. When he reached California, Pecos Bill crashed. It was the force of his fall that is said to have created Death Valley. In actuality, some rocks in the deepest part of the Grand Canyon date back to about two billion years ago. The Colorado River began forming the Grand Canyon about six million years ago. Over centuries, the water eroded the layers of rock, and the walls of the canyon were created. More erosion occurred later as a result of wind, rain, and melting snow. Death Valley is a desert in California and Nevada. It contains the lowest point in the Western Hemisphere at 282 feet below sea level.

No one is quite sure how Pecos Bill died. One version says he laughed himself to death after listening to silly questions a man from Boston asked him about the West.

Use with page 15.

**Week 1 • Day 3**

**Sequencing**

1. **Look at each picture. Number the events in the order in which they happened in the story. Write a sentence for each.**

2. **Four words from the story are hidden in the puzzle. The definition of each word is given below. Shade in the letters for each word, reading left to right and top to bottom. The remaining letters will spell the name of a real cool cowboy two times.**

   a piece of writing

   laughingly

   attributed with

   a particular form of something

| a | p | r | t | e | i | c |
|---|---|---|---|---|---|---|
| c | o | l | e | s | a | b |
| m | u | s | i | i | n | l |
| g | l | y | l | c | p | r |
| e | d | e | i | t | c | e |
| o | d | v | s | e | b | r |
| i | s | l | l | i | o | n |

**Read a story about an imaginary character. On another sheet of paper, write five events from the character's life in the order in which they happened.**

# Wild Birds

*Some addition problems will require regrouping several times. The steps look like this.*

| 1. *Add the ones column. Regroup if needed.* | 2. *Add the 10s column. Regroup if needed.* | 3. *Add the 100s column. Regroup if needed.* | 4. *Continue working through each column in order.* |
|---|---|---|---|
| $\begin{array}{r} ^{1} \\ 37{,}462 \\ +\ 22{,}798 \\ \hline 0 \end{array}$ | $\begin{array}{r} ^{11} \\ 37{,}462 \\ +\ 22{,}798 \\ \hline 60 \end{array}$ | $\begin{array}{r} ^{111} \\ 37{,}462 \\ +\ 22{,}798 \\ \hline 260 \end{array}$ | $\begin{array}{r} ^{111} \\ 37{,}462 \\ +\ 22{,}798 \\ \hline 60{,}260 \end{array}$ |

Add. Then use the code to finish the fun fact below.

bald eagle

Z. 953 + 418    B. 295 + 337    R. 418 + 793    Q. 565 + 957    S. 862 + 339    X. 478 + 283

falcon

I. 2,428 + 6,679    C. 1,566 + 2,487    Y. 3,737 + 6,418    A. 9,289 + 4,735    Y. 8,754 + 368

vulture

L. 57,854 + 45,614    P. 29,484 + 46,592    E. 36,238 + 46,135    F. 67,139 + 25,089

owl

D. 240,669 + 298,727    O. 476,381 + 175,570    R. 882,948 + 176,524

**What do all of these birds have in common?**

**They are** ____ ____ ____ ____ ____   ____ ____
632   9,107   1,211   539,396   1,201    651,951   92,228

____ ____ ____ ____ .
76,076   1,059,472   82,373   10,155

# Letter Match

Match the cursive letters to their partners.

| Cursive | Print | Cursive | Print |
|---|---|---|---|
| F | A | R | N |
| J | B | Z | O |
| B | C | V | P |
| L | D | P | Q |
| A | E | N | R |
| H | F | S | S |
| E | G | Q | T |
| K | H | Y | U |
| D | I | X | V |
| M | J | W | W |
| I | K | U | X |
| G | L | O | Y |
| C | M | T | Z |

# Eating Your Words

To "eat your words" is an expression called an idiom. Idioms can't be taken literally. To understand them, you have to know their special meanings.

Lucy said we'd lose the game, but we won. Now she'll have to eat her words.

**Name**

**Foods** Complete each of these idioms by putting the name of a food on each blank. If you don't know the idiom, put in your best guess.

be a couch ________________ (sit around, be lazy)

walk on ________________ (be very cautious)

in a ________________ (have a big problem)

spill the ________________ (give away a secret)

a piece of ________________ (something that's very easy)

like two ________________ in a pod (to be very similar)

go ________________ (go crazy)



**Similes** Expressions that compare two things using the words "as" or "like" are called similes. Complete each of these popular similes by putting the name of an animal on each blank. If you don't know the simile, put in your best guess.

as wise as a/an __________

as strong as a/an __________

as proud as a/an __________

as quiet as a/an __________

as sly as a/an __________

as stubborn as a/an __________

as busy as a/an __________

as gentle as a/an __________

as graceful as a/an __________



**Draw** a picture that illustrates the meaning of one of the idioms in this mini-book. Write the idiom at the bottom of the page.

____________________________________________

____________________________________________



Scholastic Inc. *Summer Express: Between Grades 4 & 5*

**Parts of the Body** Complete each of the idioms on these two pages by putting the name of a part of the body on each blank. If you don't know the idiom, put in your best guess.

be all ________ (be eager to listen)

hold your ________ (be silent)

have your ________ in the clouds (to daydream)

make your ________ water (look and smell tasty)

get it off your ________ (make a confession)



get a pat on your ________ (be praised)

make your ________ stand on end (be scary)

be all ________ (be awkward or clumsy)

stick your ________ out (take a risk)

button your ________ (keep quiet)

pull someone's ________ (fool someone)

catch your ________ (be noticed)

on your ________ (be alert)

give someone a ________ (help someone)



**Animals** Complete each of these idioms by putting the name of an animal on each blank. If you don't know the idiom, put in your best guess.

have a ________ in your throat (be hoarse)

raining ________ and ________ (rain hard)

be a ________ (feel fearful or anxious)

have ________ in your stomach (feel nervous)

________ around (play noisily)

smell a ________ (suspect something's wrong)

have ________ in your pants (feel restless)





**Create your own** similes by completing each of the phrases below. Try to make your similes as descriptive as possible.

as funny as ________

as noisy as ________

as scary as ________

as fast as ________

as playful as ________

as angry as ________

# Helping Your Child Get Ready: Week 2

These are the skills your child will be working on this week.

**Math**
- rounding and estimating
- reading tables and charts
- word problems

**Reading**
- following directions

**Writing**
- elaborating
- combining sentences

**Vocabulary**
- compound words

**Grammar**
- parts of speech
- commas

**Here are some activities you and your child might enjoy.**

**Fantastic Stats** Your child can use a calculator to create fantastic stats about him- or herself. For instance, have your child figure out how many times he or she has breathed since birth. Here's how:

**1.** Figure out a breath rate for one minute. **2.** Find how many breaths in one hour (multiply by 60). **3.** Find how many breaths in 1 day (multiply breaths per hour by 24). **4.** Find how many breaths in one year (multiply breaths per day by 365). **5.** Find how many breaths in the *n* years he or she has been alive (multiply breaths per year by *n*).

**30-Second Rhyme-Around** Give your child 30 seconds to think of as many rhymes as possible for a given word. Start off with words that are easier to rhyme (like *cat*), and work up to more challenging ones.

**Word Expert** Boost your child's vocabulary by playing Word Expert. Tell him or her that for each word you say, he or she must give you an antonym, a synonym, and an example of the word. For example, for *awesome*, a synonym might be *amazing*, an antonym might be *terrible*, and an example could be the *Taj Mahal*.

**Family Newsletter** Encourage your budding journalist by having him or her write a family newsletter. It can include news, weather reports, movie and book reviews, upcoming events, and even advertisements.

**Your child might enjoy reading the following books:**

*School Stories*
*by Paro Anand*

*The Hostile Hospital*
*by Lemony Snicket*

*The Brilliant World of Tom Gates*
*by Liz Pichon*

_________________________ 's Incentive Chart: Week 2

Name Here

This week, I plan to read __________ minutes each day.

CHART YOUR PROGRESS HERE.

| Week 1 | Day 1 | Day 2 | Day 3 | Day 4 | Day 5 |
|---|---|---|---|---|---|
|  I read for... | minutes | minutes | minutes | minutes | minutes |
| Put a sticker to show you completed each day's work. | | | | | |

# Congratulations!

Wow! You did a great job this week!

Place sticker here.

Parent or Caregiver's Signature ________________________________

# Bee Riddle

**Riddle: What did the farmer get when he tried to reach the beehive?**

Round each number. Then use the Decoder to solve the riddle by filling in the spaces at the bottom of the page.

1. Round 7 to the nearest ten ______
2. Round 23 to the nearest ten ______
3. Round 46 to the nearest ten ______
4. Round 92 to the nearest ten ______
5. Round 203 to the nearest hundred ______
6. Round 420 to the nearest hundred ______
7. Round 588 to the nearest hundred ______
8. Round 312 to the nearest hundred ______
9. Round 549 to the nearest hundred ______
10. Round 710 to the nearest hundred ______

## Decoder

400............ **A**
800............ **W**
30............ **O**
10............ **Y**
25............ **E**
500............ **I**
210............ **J**
20............ **L**
40............ **C**
700............ **U**
90............ **S**
100............ **T**
600............ **G**
95............ **F**
50............ **N**
550............ **V**
300............ **Z**
7............ **H**
200............ **Z**

**A "B** ___ ___ ___ ___ **"** ___ ___ ___ ___ ___ ___

10 5 8 1 4 9 7 3 6 2

# Make It Interesting

*A sentence can be very simple. This sentence tells who did what.*

**The crew worked.**

*As you write and revise your writing, add details about people, places, or things, or about where, when, and what happens. This will make your writing more interesting. Here's how the sentence above was revised several times. Each sentence gives a little more information.*

**The construction crew worked.**
**The construction crew worked quickly.**
**The construction crew worked quickly to clear the rubble.**
**The construction crew worked quickly to clear the rubble at the building site.**
**The construction crew worked quickly yesterday to clear the rubble at the building site.**

Rewrite each sentence four times. Add new details each time to tell more about whom or what, how, where, and when.

**The children played.**

1. ______________________________
2. ______________________________
3. ______________________________
4. ______________________________

**A package arrived.**

1. ______________________________
2. ______________________________
3. ______________________________
4. ______________________________

**Rewrite the following sentence several times on a sheet of paper. Remove a detail each time until you are left with a very simple sentence.**

**The excited team cheered wildly after winning the cricket match.**

Use with page 26.



# Green Gift

"Poor Grandma! I wish there was some way we could cheer her up," Amy said to her brother Mark.

Grandma had fallen and broken her leg. The doctor said she would be in a cast for six weeks. Grandma was very active and loved to work in her garden, so she would not enjoy sitting in her chair waiting for her leg to heal.

"I have an idea," said Mark. "I saw some pictures of terrariums in a magazine. Terrariums are little indoor gardens that can be grown in glass jars. Let's make a terrarium for Grandma, so she can enjoy a garden in her house."

Amy thought Mark had a great idea, so the two of them found the magazine article with the directions for making a terrarium and showed their mom. She agreed that a terrarium would be a perfect gift for Grandma. She helped Amy and Mark find a large, clear glass bottle, which they cleaned and checked for leaks. After a trip to the garden shop to buy the materials, they were ready to assemble the terrarium.

First, they put a small layer of charcoal and gravel drainage material at the bottom of the bottle. This would keep the soil from getting too damp.

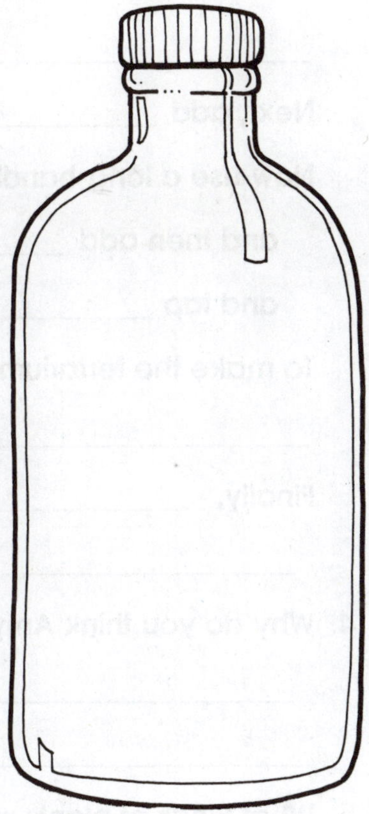

**Draw a layer of charcoal and gravel at the bottom of the bottle.**

Next, they added a layer of dark, rich soil.

**Draw a layer of dark soil on top of the drainage materials.**

Now they were ready to add the plants. Mark used a long-handled spoon to tap out holes in the soil. Amy had chosen two plants at the garden shop. One was tall with long, thin, green leaves. The other was short with bright pink flowers. Mark placed the plants in the holes and gently tapped the soil down over their roots.

**Draw the two plants Mark and Amy planted.**

To make the terrarium even more colourful, Amy placed some colorful rocks and bright green moss around the plants.

**Draw the colourful rocks and green moss that Amy added to the terrarium.**

Finally, Mark and Amy lightly watered the plants by pouring water through a small funnel at the top of the bottle. Now the terrarium was ready to take to Grandma.

When Amy and Mark showed Grandma her new terrarium, she was so happy. Now she had a beautiful little garden to enjoy right inside her home.

Mark and Amy want to make another terrarium for their Aunt Hilda's birthday, but they lost the magazine article with the directions. Help them make a new set of directions.

1. Make a list of all the materials Mark and Amy needed to assemble the terrarium.

_______________

_______________

_______________

2. What must be done to the bottle before adding the materials to it? _______________

_______________

3. Tell how to assemble the terrarium. Be sure to use the steps in correct order.

First, _______________

_______________

Next, add _______________

Now use a long-handled spoon to _______________

and then add _______________

and tap _______________

To make the terrarium more colourful, place _______________

_______________

Finally, _______________

_______________

4. Why do you think Amy only chose two plants for the terrarium? _______________

_______________

_______________

5. What kinds of plants would not be good choices for a terrarium? _______________

_______________

_______________

**Cut a label off a product your family is finished using. On another sheet of paper, write three questions involving the directions on the label for using the product. Give the label and the questions to someone in your family to answer.**

# How's Your Heart Rate?

**You Need:**
- stopwatch or watch with a second hand
- tennis ball

Animals have hearts that do the same job as a person's heart. An animal's heart beats to pump blood through its body. What's different about an animal heart and a human heart? The number of times it beats in a minute.

Each day your heart beats about 100,000 times. That's enough times to pump almost 1,500 gallons of blood throughout your body! By the time you are 70 years old, your heart will have pumped about 38 million gallons of blood. No wonder it's important to keep your heart strong and healthy!

The number of times a heart beats in a certain amount of time is called **heart rate.** Check out the table to find some average animal heart rates. Then follow the steps to add your heart rate to the table.

| ANIMAL | HEART RATE (for one minute) |
|---|---|
| Canary | 1,000 |
| Mouse | 650 |
| Chicken | 200 |
| Cat | 110 |
| Dog | 80 |
| Adult human | 72 |
| Giraffe | 60 |
| Tiger | 45 |
| Elephant | 25 |
| Gray whale | 8 |
| You | |

## How to Find Your Heart Rate

- Place two fingers on your neck or your wrist. Move them around until you feel a pulse beat.
- Count the beats for 30 seconds. Have someone at home time you with the watch.
- Multiply the number of beats by two. That number is your heart rate for one minute.

### Hearts Are Hard Workers

To prove it, try this. Squeeze a tennis ball as hard as you can and let go. That's how hard your heart works to pump blood through your body. Now try to squeeze the ball for one minute to match your heart rate. Not too easy, is it?

Answer these questions about animals' heart rates, using the information on the table.

1. Which animal's heart beats fastest in one minute? ____________________

   Which beats slowest? ____________________

2. What do you notice about the size of the animal compared with its heart rate?

   ____________________

3. Where do you think a horse's heart rate might fit on the table? Explain your answer.

   ____________________

   ____________________

4. Which animal is your heart rate the closest to? ____________________

# Compound It All!

*A **compound word** is formed by combining two words.*

Each word below can be combined with one of the other words to form a compound word. Starting with *cookbook,* take the second word, *book,* and write it on the next line. Then choose a word from the box that will make a new compound word. Continue until you have used all the words in the box.

| house | way | walk | side | hill |
|---|---|---|---|---|
| cook | store | book | hold | up |

cook + book = cookbook

_____ + _____ = _____

_____ + _____ = _____

_____ + _____ = _____

_____ + _____ = _____

_____ + _____ = _____

_____ + _____ = _____

_____ + _____ = _____

_____ + _____ = _____

Starting with the word *quarterback,* continue to make compound words as you did above using the words from the box.

| mate | stick | back | quarter | yard | room | ball |
|---|---|---|---|---|---|---|

_____ + _____ = _____

_____ + _____ = _____

_____ + _____ = _____

_____ + _____ = _____

_____ + _____ = _____

_____ + _____ = _____

**Read a page from a book you are reading, a newspaper column, or a magazine article. On another sheet of paper, list the compound words you find.**

# Attack of the Massive Melon!

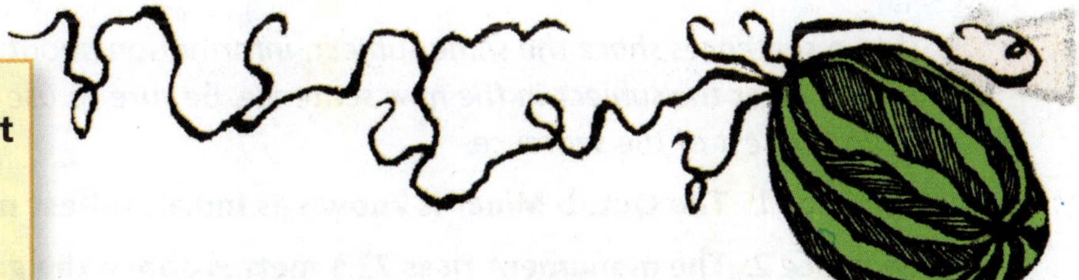

**Don't read this story yet! Give it to a partner and ask him or her to tell you the parts of speech under the blanks below. You give a word for each part of speech, and your partner writes it in the blank. Then he or she writes the words in the story and reads the story aloud.**

1. ______________ ADJECTIVE ENDING IN *EST*
2. ______________ NOUN
3. ______________ PLURAL NOUN
4. ______________ ADJECTIVE
5. ______________ NOUN
6. ______________ VERB ENDING IN *ING*
7. ______________ FAMOUS PERSON
8. ______________ ADJECTIVE
9. ______________ ADVERB
10. ______________ NOUN
11. ______________ FAVOURITE FOOD
12. ______________ NUMBER
13. ______________ BODY PART
14. ______________ VERB

I decided that I was going to grow the ________ (1) garden in the world. I used a ________ (2) to dig holes in the backyard, then I spread seeds and ________ (3) all around. Pretty soon, my garden started looking ________ (4). I had planted ________ (5) seeds, but a watermelon started ________ (6) out of the ground! It grew and grew. This watermelon became bigger than ________ (7)! Mom said we should eat it before it turned ________ (8). So every day I climbed ________ (9) up a ________ (10), then leaped to the top of the melon and cut off huge pieces. We made watermelon shakes, peanut butter and watermelon sandwiches, and ________ (11) with watermelon sauce. I've eaten almost nothing but melon for the last ________ (12) months! Mom said, "Don't look a gift horse in the ________ (13)." I sure learned a lesson: Don't bite off more than you can ________ (14)!

# Hot Subjects

*If two sentences share the same subject, information about the subject can be written as a phrase after the subject in the new sentence. Be sure to use commas to set apart the phrase from the rest of the sentence.*

*Sentence 1:* **The Qutub Minar is known as India's tallest man-made monument.**

*Sentence 2:* **The monument rises 72.5 metres above the ground.**

*Combined:* **The Qutub Minar, India's tallest man-made monument, rises 72.5 metres above the ground.**

Read the sentences. Combine the ideas in each pair into one sentence by including information in a phrase after the subject in the sentence.

1. **The Caspian Sea is the world's largest lake.**
   **The lake covers an area which is larger than entire state of Rajasthan.**

   ______________________________________________

2. **The Komodo dragon is a member of the monitor family.**
   **It can grow to a length of 10 feet.**

   ______________________________________________

3. **Our closest star is the sun.**
   **It is estimated to be more than 27,000,000°F.**

   ______________________________________________

4. **APJ Abdul Kalam was the 11th President of India.**
   **He worked as a scientist for almost 40 years.**

   ______________________________________________

5. **Uttar Pradesh is the nation's largest producer of sugar.**
   **It produces almost 70 per cent of the sugar produced in India.**

   ______________________________________________

6. **Sachin Tendulkar is one of greatest cricketer of all times.**
   **He is the first batsman to score a double century in a One Day International**

   ______________________________________________

# A Penny Saved Is a Penny Earned

Write a number sentence for each problem. Solve.

| | |
|---|---|
| A. **Aimee and her 2 sisters are saving to buy a camera. Aimee has ₹12000.89. Each of her sisters has $28000.53. How much money do all the girls have combined?** | B. **Katie has ₹2395 in her purse, ₹1723 in her bank, and ₹7682 in her savings account. What is the total amount of Katie's money?** |
| C. **Jonah worked in the yard for 3 days. The first day he earned ₹70.96. The second day he earned ₹20 more than the first day. The third day he earned ₹20 less than the first day. How much did Jonah earn altogether?** | D. **Jack has ₹900.50. He also has 79 coins of ₹5 and 139 coins of 50 paise. How much money does he have altogether?** |
| E. **Kelsey has 478 coins in her collection. The ₹1 coins equal ₹79.00, and the cost of 25 paise equal ₹99.75. How much is Kelsey's collection worth in all?** | F. **Claire bought lemonade for herself and two friends. Each cup costs ₹17.50. How much did Claire spend in all?** |

**On another sheet of paper, write a word problem with a sum equal to ₹41.68.**

# Triple the Fun

*When you write, you may want to list three or more items or ideas in a series in a single sentence. Be sure to use a comma after each item in a series except after the last item.*

**Max dressed quickly, ate breakfast, and raced out the door.**
**Luis, Jamie, Leroy, and Sam met Max at the baseball field.**
**They were hopeful, excited, and nervous about their first game.**

Answer each question below in a complete sentence. Use commas where they are needed. Make sure each sentence begins and ends correctly. Remember to check your spelling.

1. **What are the titles of three books you've read recently or would like to read? Remember to underline the title of each book.**

   ______________________________________________

2. **What are four of the planets in our solar system closer to the sun than Pluto?**

   ______________________________________________

3. **What are three green, leafy vegetables?**

   ______________________________________________

4. **What countries would you like to visit? Include at least three in your answer.**

   ______________________________________________

5. **What months fall between January and July?**

   ______________________________________________

6. **What three things have you done today to help out at home?**

   ______________________________________________

7. **What states or bodies of water border your state?**

   ______________________________________________

8. **What activities do you and your friends enjoy in the summer?**

   ______________________________________________

9. **Who are some of the most important people in your life?**

   ______________________________________________

**Make up some questions like the ones above and challenge someone you know to answer them on a sheet of paper. Correct the sentences.**

# Helping Your Child Get Ready: Week 3

These are the skills your child will be working on this week.

**Maths**
- subtraction with regrouping
- subtraction with multiple regrouping

**Reading**
- predicting
- drawing conclusions

**Writing**
- combining sentences
- sentence variety

**Vocabulary**
- prefixes

**Grammar**
- proofreading

**Handwriting**
- lowercase cursive letters

**Here are some activities you and your child might enjoy.**

**30-Second Synonyms** Give your child 30 seconds to come up with as many synonyms as possible for the word *happy*. Then try *sad*.

**Cricket Weather** Can you hear crickets chirping where you live? If you can, here's a fun way to practice some math skills. Tell your child to count how many times a cricket chirps in 15 seconds. Have him or her add 37 to that number. The sum is the temperature in degrees Fahrenheit!

**Fire Safety Plan** Ask your child to create a fire safety plan booklet. He or she can draw a map on each page to describe how each family member should escape from your home. Another page can explain where family members should go if they need to leave the house quickly.

**Set a Family Record** How long can your child hop? It's time to set a family record! Have him or her choose an activity and see how long he or she can do it. Then see if he or she can break the record the next day.

**Your child might enjoy reading the following books:**

*Dork Diaries: Once upon a Dork*
*by Rachel Renee Russell*

*The Tree with a Travelling Heart*
*by Paro Anand*

*Animal Stories*
*by Ruskin Bond*

____________________ **'s Incentive Chart: Week 3**

Name Here

This week, I plan to read __________ minutes each day.

CHART YOUR PROGRESS HERE.

| Week 1 | Day 1 | Day 2 | Day 3 | Day 4 | Day 5 |
| --- | --- | --- | --- | --- | --- |
|  I read for... | minutes | minutes | minutes | minutes | minutes |
| Put a sticker to show you completed each day's work. | | | | | |

# Congratulations!

Wow! You did a great job this week!

Place sticker here.

**Parent or Caregiver's Signature** ____________________________

# Checkmate

*To subtract with regrouping, follow these steps.*

1. *Subtract the ones column. Regroup if needed.*

```
   2 11
   4 3 1
 - 2 6 6
 -------
       5
```

2. *Subtract the tens column. Regroup if needed.*

```
    12
   3 2 11
   4 3 1
 - 2 6 6
 -------
     6 5
```

3. *Subtract the hundreds column. Regroup if needed.*

```
    12
   3 2 11
   4 3 1
 - 2 6 6
 -------
   1 6 5
```

Subtract. Cross out the chess piece with the matching difference. The last piece standing is the winner of the match.

63

464

| | | |
|---|---|---|
| 956 − 492 = ____ | 239 − 176 = ____ | 842 − 426 = ____ |

179

| | | |
|---|---|---|
| 153 − 80 = ____ | 351 − 172 = ____ | 983 − 284 = ____ |

699

416

| | | |
|---|---|---|
| 526 − 286 = ____ | 643 − 479 = ____ | 258 − 139 = ____ |

73

240

| | |
|---|---|
| 932 − 426 = ____ | 852 − 476 = ____ |

164

506

119

☐ is left standing.

479

376

# All Aboard!

*A **prefix** is a word part that is added to the beginning of a word and changes its meaning. Here are some common prefixes and their meanings.*

| | | | | | |
|---|---|---|---|---|---|
| **a-** | on | **multi-** | many, much | **super-** | above, beyond |
| **anti-** | against | **non-** | not | **trans-** | across |
| **im-** | not | **over-** | too much | **un-** | not |
| **in-** | not | **pre-** | before | **under-** | below, less than |
| **inter-** | among, between | **re-** | again | | |
| **mis-** | wrong | **re-** | back | | |

Here are some words with these prefixes. Use the information from the chart to write what you think each word means. Then use a dictionary to check your definitions. Make corrections if needed.

1. **aboard** ____________
2. **supervisor** ____________
3. **multicoloured** ____________
4. **misunderstood** ____________
5. **international** ____________
6. **preheat** ____________
7. **nonstop** ____________
8. **transcontinental** ____________
9. **uncomfortable** ____________
10. **overpriced** ____________
11. **review** ____________
12. **unbelievable** ____________
13. **inexpensive** ____________
14. **underweight** ____________
15. **impatient** ____________
16. **antifreeze** ____________

**What other prefixes do you know? On another sheet of paper, list them along with their meanings. Knowing what a prefix means can help you to figure out the meaning of an unfamiliar word.**

# Letter Match

Match the cursive letters to their partners.

| Cursive | Print | Cursive | Print |
|---|---|---|---|
| *j* | a | *q* | n |
| *m* | b | *w* | o |
| *c* | c | *o* | p |
| *a* | d | *z* | q |
| *h* | e | *v* | r |
| *k* | f | *p* | s |
| *e* | g | *y* | t |
| *d* | h | *s* | u |
| *f* | i | *u* | v |
| *b* | j | *n* | w |
| *i* | k | *t* | x |
| *l* | l | *r* | y |
| *g* | m | *x* | z |

# Sentence Building

*When you write about something, try to include interesting details. Sometimes you can take the important details from several related sentences and add them to the main sentence.*

**Kyle and Jim had a great plan.**
**They're my brothers.**
**The plan was for a tree house.**

*Now here's a sentence that combines all the important details.*

**My brothers Kyle and Jim had a great plan for a tree house.**

Read each group of sentences. Take the important details from the two related sentences and add them to the main sentence to make one sentence.

1. **My brothers built a tree house. They built it in the old oak tree. It's in our backyard.**

   ______________________________

2. **Jim made a ladder for the tree house. He made it out of rope. It is sturdy.**

   ______________________________

3. **Kyle bought paint. The paint was brown. He bought a litre.**

   ______________________________

4. **Kyle and Jim finished painting. They painted the walls. It took an hour.**

   ______________________________

5. **Jim painted a sign. He painted "no trespassing." The sign is on the tree house door.**

   ______________________________

6. **A squirrel leaped into their tree house. It leaped from a branch. It was curious.**

   ______________________________

7. **The visitor startled my brothers. It was unexpected. My brothers were unsuspecting.**

   ______________________________

8. **The squirrel leaped out of the tree house. It was frightened. It was in a big hurry.**

   ______________________________

**Write three short sentences on a sheet of paper about a funny experience. Then try to combine them into one sentence. Which sounds better, one sentence with lots of details or two or three shorter sentences each with one detail? Why?**

# Test Time

**Making predictions** *is using information from a story to determine what will happen next.*

On Monday, Mrs Khanna announced to her students that they would have their test covering the 29 states and capitals on Friday. In addition to knowing each state's capital, the students would have to be able to fill in all the states' names on the map of India. Mrs Khanna also told the students to be sure to take special notice of their own state. She even put up a poster in front of the classroom showing the state map along with the state dance and art forms. Best friends Kevin and Matt both wanted to do well on the test, but each boy studied for the test in a very different way.

Kevin decided to wait until Thursday evening to begin studying. He thought if he learned everything on Thursday, he would be able to remember it better on Friday. After supper on Thursday evening, Kevin took his study notes into the family room so he could watch television while he studied. Mrs Khanna had given all the students an alphabetical list of the states and their capitals. Kevin read the list over and over again. Then he covered up the capitals and tried to remember what they were as he read each state's name. When he felt that he knew most of the capitals, he then took out his map and began studying where all the states were located. Because Kevin kept taking some time to watch his favourite TV shows, he did not get finished with his studying until very late. The next morning he skipped breakfast so he would not miss his bus and arrive late to school.

Matt, on the other hand, took a different approach to his studying. On Monday evening he made a set of flash cards. On one side of the card, he wrote the name of the state and on the opposite side, he wrote the state's capital. He made one card for each state. He then traced the map of India, being careful to outline each state. He took this map to the photocopy store and made several copies. Now he had some maps on which to practice writing the state names. On Tuesday, Wednesday, and Thursday, Matt spent an hour after dinner in his room studying his flash cards and practicing filling in his maps. His mom and dad also helped him by quizzing him about the state capitals while he helped with clearing the table and loading the dishwasher after dinner. On his way to school each day, Matt took his flash cards with him on the bus and practiced naming the capitals. Matt went to bed a little earlier on Thursday evening. The next morning he had a good breakfast before catching his bus. On the way to school, he looked over his map and flash cards one last time.

When the boys arrived at school on Friday, they joined their classmates and prepared to take the big test on the states. As Mrs Khanna handed out the test, Matt noticed that she had taken down the poster of their own state map. Then he received his test and, like his friend Kevin, began to work hard to do his very best.

Use with page 39.

## Week 3 • Day 3

### Making Predictions

1. **What mistakes do you think Kevin made in the way he studied?** ______________________________

2. **How was Matt's study plan different from Kevin's?** ______________________________

3. **The test Mrs Khanna gave was worth 100 points: one point for naming each state's capital correctly and one point for each state correctly filled in on the map. Write in the number of correct answers you think each boy got on his test.**

| Kevin | Matt |
|---|---|
| /100 | /100 |

**Explain why you think each boy earned the score you wrote.** ______________________________

4. **Mrs Khanna included one extra credit question on the test. What do you think it was?** ______________________________

**On another sheet of paper, write about a test you thought you were prepared for but it turned out you really were not. Read it to someone in your family.**

# Bright Idea!

*Each part of a subtraction problem has a name:*

```
    3,486   ← minuend
  − 2,371   ← subtrahend
    1,115   ← difference
```

Find each missing subtrahend by subtracting the difference from the minuend.

```
  9,416         9,416
−  [ ]        −   812
    812         8,604
```

```
 32,194
−  [ ]
  5,778
```

```
 63,417
−  [ ]
 21,759
```

```
 91,753
−  [ ]
 18,475
```

```
  8,110
−  [ ]
  3,794
```

```
 17,942
−  [ ]
  8,786
```

```
 49,234
−  [ ]
 39,741
```

```
 23,976
−  [ ]
 18,687
```

**On another sheet of paper, write two subtraction problems with missing subtrahends. Ask someone in your family to help you solve the problems.**

# Flower Fun

*To **draw conclusions** is to use the information in a story to make a logical assumption.*

Aaaaaahhhhh! It was that time of year again—time to plant flowers. Christina and her dad were trying to decide what kind of flowers to plant this year. Her dad showed her an ad in the morning paper. He wanted Christina to check it out so she could help him determine what they should buy. The two always like to surprise Christina's mom with beautiful flowers before her "big day" in May. Christina was surprised to see Flower Power was having a sale. She knew they had better hurry to the store.

FLOWER POWER SALE
Beautiful flowers of all kinds
— annuals and perennials—
are all on sale — 25% OFF!
All pots and hanging baskets
are on sale, too
Buy one, get one FREE!
Reg. ₹99.99 to ₹999.99
Hurry! Sale ends Tuesday!
Flower Power
2418 Harbor Ave.

1. **What time of year is it?** ______________________________

2. **Circle the day in May on which Christina and her dad want her mother to enjoy beautiful flowers.**

   **Father's Day** **Earth Day** **Mother's Day** **Easter**

3. **Circle why Christina and her dad will probably go to Flower Power today.**

   **because they are having a sale**

   **because they want to plant today**

   **because the two always plant flowers together**

4. **Why was Christina surprised that Flower Power was having a sale?** ______________

   ______________________________

   ______________________________

5. **Why might Christina and her dad want to buy new pots or hanging baskets?**

   ______________________________

6. **Why does the ad say to hurry?** ______________________________

   ______________________________

# Behind the Special Effects in Today's Hit Movies

Find and mark the ten grammar errors.

Dear State-of-the-Art,

Recently, I seen the movie *Detonation*, starring Arnold Morphus. It had a lot of great special effect. But, the part I likeded best come near the end. There were not no car chases, and not even any space aliens in the scene. The two characters was just talking. How did they do that?

Signed,

Curious

Dear Curious,

The part of the movie that you liked is called *acting.* Acting requires that the stars act, talk, and make gestures just like real people. Though acting in todays' movies is quite rare, believe it or not, in the olden days, acting was actually quite common in movies!

Signed,

State-of-the-Art

Dear State-of-the-Art,

How did they make the four cockroaches speak its lines in the movie *Roach Motel*?

Signed,

PUZZLED

Dear Puzzled,

This is an easy one! They just hold up cue cards. The roach read their lines right off the cue cards.

Signed,

State-of-the-Art

# Show Time

*Sometimes a writer can change the order of the words in a sentence to make it more interesting.*

**The telephone rang just as the girls were about to leave.**
**Just as the girls were about to leave, the telephone rang.**

**Gina decided to answer it in spite of the time.**
**In spite of the time, Gina decided to answer it.**

*Do not forget to add a comma when you begin a sentence with a clause or a phrase that cannot stand alone as in the second and last sentences.*

Rewrite each sentence by changing the order of the words.

1. **Marta watched for the bus while Gina answered the phone.**

2. **The caller hung up just as Gina said "Hello."**

3. **The girls were going to miss the one o'clock show unless they hurried.**

4. **The bus had already come and gone by the time they got to the corner.**

5. **The next bus to town finally showed up after the girls had waited a half hour.**

6. **The girls decided to catch the four o'clock show because they missed the earlier show.**

7. **They wouldn't have to stand in line later because Gina bought the tickets first.**

8. **Gina and Marta were at the theater by three o'clock even though it was early.**

9. **They bought a tub of popcorn and drinks once they were inside.**

# Helping Your Child Get Ready: Week 4

These are the skills your child will be working on this week.

**Maths**
- geometry
- multiplication facts

**Reading**
- drawing conclusions
- reading for details

**Writing**
- revising

**Vocabulary**
- suffixes

**Grammar**
- parts of speech
- run-on sentences

**Here are some activities you and your child might enjoy.**

**Egg-citing Science** Here's a quick and easy science activity. Ask your child if he or she thinks an egg will float in a bowl of water. Have him or her try it. Then add salt, one teaspoon at a time. Does this make a difference? Have him or her do research to find out why.

**Zero Is a Hero** To help your child understand how important zero is, have him or her look at a few of your grocery store receipts. Whenever a zero appears, have him or her transpose it. For example, .07 would become .70. Have your child add up the new numbers and compare the old and new totals.

**Word Sleuths** Give your child a newspaper and a highlighter pen. Have him or her search the newspaper trying to find five words he or she doesn't know. Model how to find the meaning of the word (using context clues, the etymology of the word, or the dictionary).

**Survey Says . . .** What is each family member's favourite treat? Have your child survey the family and share the results.

| | Cake | Brownies | Cookies | Cupcakes |
|---|---|---|---|---|
| JOSE | ✓ | | | ✓ |
| JUAN | ✓ | | ✓ | ✓ |
| CARLOS | ✓ | ✓ | ✓ | ✓ |
| ROSA | | ✓ | ✓ | |

**Your child might enjoy reading the following books:**

*Goosebumps: Checkout Time at the Dead-End Hotel*
*by R.L. Stine*

*Monster Slick and the Magic Umbrella*
*by Sanket Pethkar*

*Pippi Longstocking*
*by Astrid Lindgren*

________________________'s Incentive Chart: Week 4

Name Here

This week, I plan to read ________ minutes each day.

CHART YOUR PROGRESS HERE.

| Week 1 | Day 1 | Day 2 | Day 3 | Day 4 | Day 5 |
|---|---|---|---|---|---|
|  I read for... | minutes | minutes | minutes | minutes | minutes |
| Put a sticker to show you completed each day's work. | | | | | |

# Congratulations!

Wow! You did a great job this week!

Place sticker here.

Parent or Caregiver's Signature ________________________________

# The State of Apples

*A **suffix** is a group of letters that are added to the end of a word and can add meaning to it. Some common suffixes and their meanings are listed in the box.*

| | | | |
|---|---|---|---|
| **-ous** | full of | **-ward** | direction |
| **-less** | without | **-ity** | condition of |
| **-ment** | action or process | **-en** | to make |
| **-ent** | one who | **-ology** | science or study of |
| **-an** | relating to | **-ily** | in what manner |

One state in the United State grows enough apples for everyone in the world to have 8 kg of apples a year. Do you know which state this is? To find out, use the suffixes to write a word for each definition. The letters in the boxes will answer the question.

1. **in the direction of the east** _ _ _ _ _ ☐ _ _ _
2. **in a hearty manner** _ _ ☐ _ _ _ _ _
3. **one who resides in a place** _ _ ☐ _ _ _ _ _
4. **full of treachery** _ _ _ _ _ ☐ _ _ _ _ _
5. **relating to India** _ _ _ ☐ _ _
6. **action of governing** _ _ _ _ _ ☐ _ _ _ _
7. **the study of animals** _ _ _ _ _ ☐ _
8. **the condition of being necessary** _ _ _ _ _ _ _ ☐ _
9. **without noise** _ ☐ _ _ _ _ _ _ _
10. **to make weak** _ _ _ _ _ ☐

# Geometric Terminology

Match the geometric terms on the left side of the page to the correct shape on the right. Use a ruler or a straightedge to draw a line from the term to the shape (dot to dot). Your line will pass through a number and a letter. The number tells you where to write your letter in the code boxes to answer the riddle below.

**What should you do if Godzilla suddenly starts to cry?**

- pentagon •
- ray •
- intersecting lines •
- rectangle •
- line •
- triangle •
- point •
- perpendicular lines •
- circle •
- line segment •
- square •
- hexagon •
- parallel lines •
- octagon •

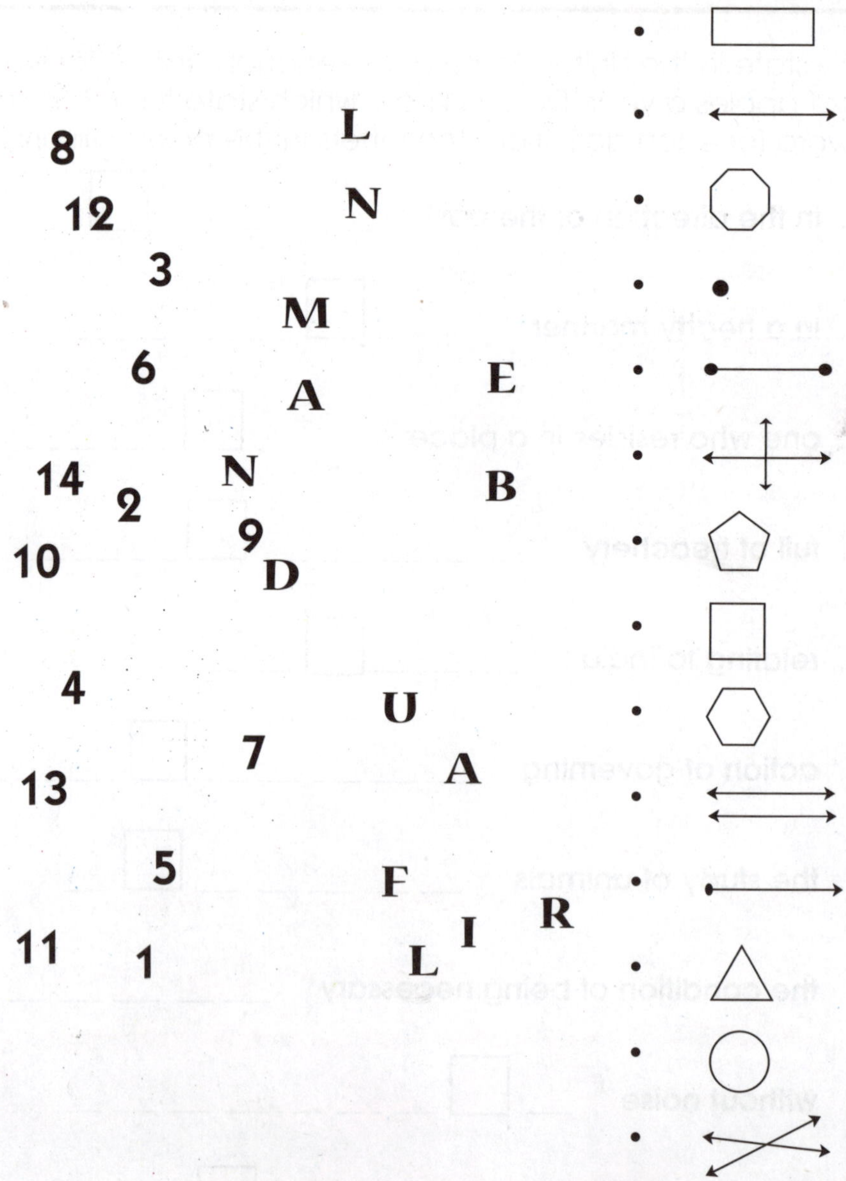


| 1 | 2 | 3 | 4 | | 5 | 6 | | 7 | 8 | 9 | 10 | 11 | 12 | 13 | 14 |
|---|---|---|---|---|---|---|---|---|---|---|---|---|---|---|---|
| | | | | | | | | | | | | | | | |

# A Timely Business

*To **draw conclusions** is to use the information in a story to make a logical assumption.*

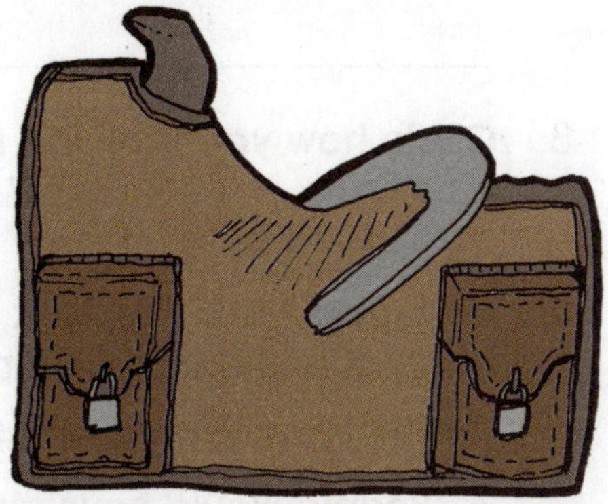

**April 15, 1860**—The mail did get through! The Pony Express mail delivery service is happy to announce that its riders finished the first complete run from Missouri to California in the United States of America. It originated on April 3.

For those of you unfamiliar with the Pony Express, this impressive American service employs men who ride fast ponies or horses, relay-style, across a 3163-km trail. These men carry letters and small packages. They promise delivery from one end of the trail to the other in 10 days or less!

Finally, there is a way to communicate long distance with friends and acquaintances. You will not have to rely on slow boats or stagecoaches. About 180 riders, 400 fast horses, and 190 Pony Express stations make up the Pony Express. Its riders are generally of small build, and many are teenagers. A day's work consists of about a 75-mile trip, with stops at several stations. The stations are about 10 to 15 miles apart. Riders earn about $100 to $150 (approximately ₹10,000) a month.

Currently, it costs $5.00 (approximately ₹320) to send 15 grams of mail. However, the price could fall to $1.00 (approximately ₹60) in the future if the service continues to do well. Mail usually travels at a rate of about 320 km a day.

The Pony Express operates both day and night to ensure timely delivery of important letters and packages. Its riders work in all kinds of weather and even face attacks by native Indians. Be kind if you see a hard-working rider.

**October 26, 1861**—Sad news for the Pony Express. After operating for only about 19 months, the service closed its doors today. This came just two days after the opening of the transcontinental telegraph, a device that has revolutionised long-distance communication. Needless to say, the Pony Express faces huge monetary losses.

The closing comes just months after the Pony Express service boasted of a 7-day, 17-hour delivery from St. Joseph, Missouri, to Sacramento, California. The record-breaking ride delivered a copy of President Abraham Lincoln's first address to Congress.

1. **Underline each statement that could have happened after the pony express closed.**

   **People relied on boats and stagecoaches for mail delivery.**

   **Pony express riders had to find new jobs.**

   **There were many fast horses for sale.**

   **News traveled more quickly by means of the transcontinental telegraph.**

2. **How do you think people felt about the Pony Express closing.** ______________________

______________________________________________

______________________________________________

3. **Circle how you think the pony express riders felt after the pony express closed.**

**relieved** **sad** **defeated** **enlightened**

4. **Underline what you think would have happened to the pony express if it had stayed open after the transcontinental telegraph opened.**

**The Pony Express would have hired more riders.**

**People would have stopped using the pony express once they realised how much more efficient it was to communicate over distance by means of the transcontinental telegraph.**

**The pony express would have built several more trails for their riders to use.**

5. **Find words from the story to match each definition. Then circle each word in the puzzle. The words go across, up, down, or backward.**

**hires and pays** ______________________

**having a strong impact on** ______________________

**made up of** ______________________

**began** ______________________

**people you know, but not very well** ______________________

**brought about a major change** ______________________

| | | | | | | | | | | | | | | |
|---|---|---|---|---|---|---|---|---|---|---|---|---|---|---|
| K | A | C | Q | U | A | I | N | T | A | N | C | E | S | C |
| R | D | L | N | C | T | M | G | O | G | O | Z | R | Y | O |
| N | E | A | O | M | O | P | N | I | N | E | Y | P | O | N |
| H | U | C | I | V | E | R | W | Z | U | S | H | S | L | S |
| O | K | T | Q | N | D | E | I | P | C | O | I | E | P | I |
| J | S | C | I | U | E | S | M | N | L | P | J | S | M | S |
| M | A | I | R | E | T | S | F | S | A | I | Y | I | E | T |
| D | E | S | I | N | O | I | T | U | L | O | V | E | R | S |
| R | Q | O | O | R | E | V | O | L | U | T | I | O | N | E |
| Y | C | U | B | A | D | E | T | A | N | I | G | I | R | O |

**The first railroad was built in India in 1851. On another sheet of paper, write how you think this changed communication in India.**

# Two at the Zoo

**Don't read this story yet! Give it a partner and ask him or her to tell you the parts of speech under the blanks below. You give a word for each part of speech, and your partner writes it in the blank. Then he or she writes the words in the story and reads the story aloud.**

1. ____________ FRIEND'S NAME
2. ____________ ADJECTIVE
3. ____________ YOUR TOWN
4. ____________ FRIEND'S NAME
5. ____________ NOUN
6. ____________ ANIMAL
7. ____________ ADJECTIVE
8. ____________ NOUN
9. ____________ VERB
10. ____________ NOUN
11. ____________ ADJECTIVE
12. ____________ FRIEND'S NAME
13. ____________ ADJECTIVE
14. ____________ VERB
15. ____________ NOUN

The whole thing was an accident. My friend ____(1)____ and I just wanted to spend a ____(2)____ day at the ____(3)____ Zoo. Who knew that ____(4)____ would slip on a ____(5)____ and bump into the ____(6)____ cage? The door sprang open, and the ____(7)____ creature inside, which was eating a ____(8)____, ran out of the cage. It went nuts! I've never seen an animal ____(9)____ like that before! The zookeeper came out with a giant ____(10)____ to catch the ____(11)____ beast. The zookeeper's eyesight wasn't good. He caught ____(12)____ instead. Don't worry—my friend now lives in a ____(13)____ cage and can ____(14)____ all day long, or even play with a ____(15)____.

# Keep On Going

*Writers sometimes make the mistake of running together two or more sentences without telling how the ideas are related. This kind of sentence is called a* **run-on sentence.**

**The Baily Bridge in India, located in the Ladakh valley between the Dras and Suru rivers in the Himalayan mountains, was built by the Indian Army in August 1982 and is the highest bridge in the world.**

*To fix a run-on sentence, identify each complete thought or idea and break it into shorter sentences.*

**The Baily Bridge is the highest bridge in the world. It is located in the Ladakh valley between the Dras and Suru rivers in the Himalayan mountains. It was built by the Indian Army in August 1982.**

Rewrite each run-on sentence correctly. Remember to begin and end each sentence correctly.

1. **Major Dhyan Chand, the wizard of hockey, was summoned by Hitler and promised German citizenship, a high post in the German military and the chance to play for the German national side, which he declined, after he and his team defeated Germany 8-1 in the 1936 Berlin Olympics.**

2. **Snakes and Ladder, earlier known as Moksha Patamu, was initially invented as a moral lesson about karma to be taught to children but it was later commercialised and has become one of the most popular board games in the world.**

3. **It would be fantastic to have a robot to do all my chores, help do my homework, and play games I really think the day will come unfortunately, it won't come soon enough for me.**

Week 4 • Day 4
Multiplication Facts

# Under the Big Top

*The answer to a multiplication problem is called the* ***product****.*
*The numbers being multiplied are called* ***factors****.*

Multiply. Then use each product and the code to answer the riddles.

### What happened to the human cannonball at the circus?

___ 4 x 6 ___ 6 x 3 / ___ 7 x 7 ___ 3 x 4 ___ 8 x 8 / ___ 8 x 3 ___ 6 x 8 ___ 7 x 9 ___ 2 x 9 ___ 8 x 7

___ 6 x 2 ___ 8 x 9 ___ 7 x 8 / ___ 9 x 9 ___ 8 x 6 ___ 9 x 7 ___ 3 x 6 ___ 7 x 8 / ___ 7 x 6 ___ 9 x 8

___ 5 x 9 ___ 6 x 4 ___ 9 x 2 / ___ 8 x 8 ___ 4 x 3 ___ 6 x 6 ___ 6 x 3 / ___ 8 x 7 ___ 2 x 6 ___ 5 x 5 !

### What happened to the kid who ran away with the circus?

___ 3 x 8 ___ 2 x 9 / ___ 4 x 6 ___ 3 x 4 ___ 8 x 7

___ 9 x 5 ___ 6 x 7 / ___ 9 x 3 ___ 7 x 9 ___ 8 x 6 ___ 9 x 8 ___ 5 x 8

___ 6 x 8 ___ 5 x 9 / ___ 3 x 9 ___ 2 x 6 ___ 5 x 3 ___ 9 x 6 !

| | | | |
|---|---|---|---|
| A = 12 | H = 24 | O = 42 | V = 21 |
| B = 27 | I = 48 | P = 16 | W = 49 |
| C = 15 | J = 4 | Q = 28 | X = 1 |
| D = 56 | K = 54 | R = 63 | Y = 25 |
| E = 18 | L = 8 | S = 64 | Z = 2 |
| F = 81 | M = 36 | T = 45 | |
| G = 40 | N = 72 | U = 0 | |

# A Long School Year

*Have you ever accidentally left out words when you write? Whenever you write, it is always a good idea to proofread for words that may be missing. Here is an example of what to do when you want to add a missing word as you proofread.*

**I got an ^ from my friend last night.** (e-mail)

**We ^ last summer when my family was in Japan.** (met)

Read the passage below about school in Japan. Twenty-one words are missing. Figure out what they are and add them to the sentences. Use the ^ symbol to show where each missing word belongs. Then write each missing word above the sentence. Hint: Every sentence has at least one missing word.

**How would like to go to school on Saturdays? If you lived in the of Japan, that's just where you'd be each Saturday morning. I have a who lives in Japan. Yuichi explained that attend classes five and one-half a week. The day is on Saturday. I was also surprised to that the Japanese school is one of the longest in the world—over 240 days. It begins in the of April. While we have over two months off each, students in Japan get their in late July and August. School then again in fall and ends in March. The people of believe that a good is very important. Children are required to attend school from the age of six to the of fifteen. They have elementary and middle just like we do. Then most go on to school for another three years. Yuichi says that students work very because the standards are so high. He and some of his friends even extra classes after school. They all want to get into a good someday.**

**Write several sentences on a sheet of paper about something that interests you. Rewrite the sentences on another sheet of paper, this time leaving out a key word in each one. Challenge someone at home to add the missing words. Then compare the two sets of sentences.**

Use with page 56.


# Amazing Animals

All animals are fascinating, and some are truly amazing! For example, did you know that sharks' teeth are as hard as steel, or that kangaroo rats can survive longer without water than camels? Study the chart below to learn more about several amazing animals.

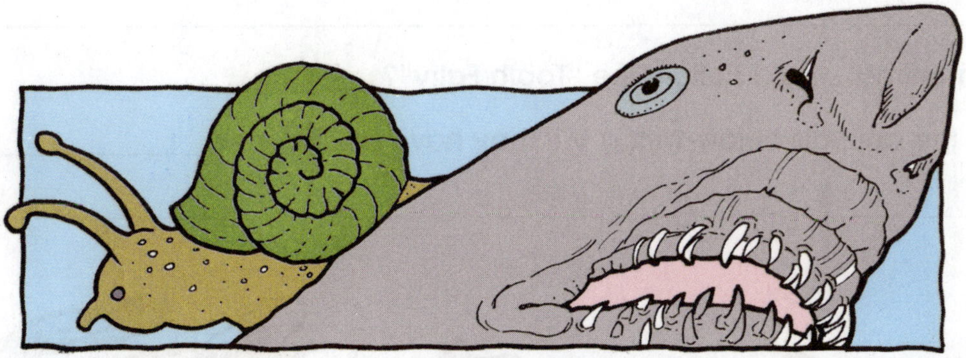

| Animal | Where It Lives | Vertebrate or Invertebrate | Fascinating Fact |
|---|---|---|---|
| albatross | near most oceans | vertebrate | can sleep while flying |
| caterpillar | all over the world | invertebrate | has three times as many muscles as humans |
| chameleon | forests in Africa and Madagascar | vertebrate | can move its eyes in two different directions at the same time |
| cockroach | all over the world | invertebrate | can live for up to a week without a head |
| crocodile | tropical climates | vertebrate | eats only about 50 meals a year |
| giant squid | oceans throughout the world | invertebrate | has eyes bigger than a human head |
| giraffe | grasslands in Africa | vertebrate | is the tallest of animals; has only seven neck bones |
| penguin | in the southern half of the world with cold ocean waters | vertebrate | has eggs kept warm by male until hatched |
| octopus | oceans throughout the world | invertebrate | has three hearts |
| shark | oceans throughout the world | vertebrate | never runs out of teeth |
| snail | almost everywhere—forests, deserts, rivers, ponds, oceans | invertebrate | can sleep for almost three years without waking up |
| sperm whale | oceans throughout the world | vertebrate | can hold its breath for up to 60 minutes |

Use with page 55.

Week 4 • Day 5

Reading for Details

1. Which animal(s) live in the ocean? ______________________

2. What do the giant squid and the chameleon have in common? ______________________

3. Which animal would delight the "Tooth Fairy"? ______________________

4. Label the animals below with a *V* if they have backbones. ______________________

5. Which animals live all, or nearly all, over the world? ______________________

6. Which animal is very muscular? ______________________

7. Which animal eats an average of about once a week? ______________________

8. Which animal can live headless for about a week? ______________________

9. What is fascinating about a chameleon's eyes? ______________________

10. Which animal is a "super snoozer"? ______________________

11. Which animal can hold its breath for nearly an hour? ______________________

12. Which animal has seven bones in its neck? ______________________

**Read about another animal. Find a fascinating fact about it to share with someone in your family.**

# Helping Your Child Get Ready: Week 5

These are the skills your child will be working on this week.

**Maths**
- multiplication with regrouping
- area and perimeter

**Reading**
- summarising
- comparing and contrasting

**Writing**
- parts of a paragraph
- topic sentences

**Vocabulary**
- word roots

**Grammar**
- subject-verb agreement

**Here are some activities you and your child might enjoy.**

**Double Meanings** Have your child figure out the two (or more!) meanings for each of these words: *bob*, *hamper*, *maroon*, *fair*. Think of more double-meaning words to challenge your child.

**Rupee Flick** In this measuring skill-building game, competitors flick a rupee across the floor or table top. The winner is the one whose coin comes to rest closest to 1 metre from the starting line.

**Root-Word Hunting** Ask your child to think of as many words as possible that have the root word *aqua*. Then have him or her figure out the meaning of this root. Try this with other roots like *graph*, *spect*, and *geo*.

**Memorise a Poem** Encourage your child to memorise a short poem. Have him or her read the poem repeatedly (a great way to build reading fluency). Suggest that he or she learn one line a day. Agree on a special treat when he or she has successfully memorised the poem.

**Your child might enjoy reading the following books:**

*The Selfish Giant*
*by Oscar Wilde*

*Sarah, Plain and Tall*
*by Patricia MacLachlan*

*The Amazing Stardust Friends #1: Step Into the Spotlight!*
*by Heather Alexander*

______________________'s Incentive Chart: Week 5

Name Here

This week, I plan to read ________ minutes each day.

CHART YOUR PROGRESS HERE.

| Week 1 | Day 1 | Day 2 | Day 3 | Day 4 | Day 5 |
|---|---|---|---|---|---|
|  I read for... | minutes | minutes | minutes | minutes | minutes |
| Put a sticker to show you completed each day's work. | | | | | |

# Congratulations!

Wow! You did a great job this week!

Place sticker here.

Parent or Caregiver's Signature ______________________________

# The Root of the Matter

*A word can have parts. The main part of a word, or* ***root****, contains the basic meaning. Here are some common roots.*

**spec, vid, vis, scop** = see
**aud** = hear
**phon, son** = sound
**tact** = touch
**clam, claim** = shout
**dic** = speak

The root is missing from one word in each sentence. Use context clues and the meaning of the roots to complete each word with its root.

1. **My grandfather listens to his old 45s on a ______ograph.**
2. **NASA lost con______ with the astronauts during reentry.**
3. **The ______or of the crowd was almost deafening.**
4. **We heard a piano ______ata by Beethoven at the concert.**
5. **Everyone in the ______ience seemed to enjoy the play.**
6. **Hometown ______tators cheered as their team ran onto the field.**
7. **The crack in the plate is barely ______ible.**
8. **Why don't you come over and watch a ______eo with us?**
9. **The suspect pro______ed that he was not guilty of the charges.**
10. **The students used a micro______e to study the plant cells.**
11. **I will ______tate the list of words so listen carefully.**

On another sheet of paper, list the words you made. Define each one in your own words. Then use a dictionary to check your definitions. Make corrections if needed.

**Here are some more common roots. Find out what each root means. Knowing these roots will help you figure out the meaning of unfamiliar words.**

| | | | | | | | | |
|---|---|---|---|---|---|---|---|---|
| act | aero | aqua | bio | cycl | fac | form | geo | gram |
| liber | loc | mar | mob | nat | pod | photo | ques | san |
| saur | scribe | sign | terr | therm | trib | voc | void | volv |

# Subject-Verb Agreement

The **subject** and **verb** in a sentence must agree in person (first, second, or third) and in number. A singular subject takes a singular verb, and a plural subject takes a plural verb.

A. **Draw one line under the subject in each sentence. Draw two lines under the verb. Then write *S* if the subject and verb are singular or *P* if they are plural.**

1. A conductor beats time with a baton. ______
2. Many musicians memorise their music. ______
3. The principal violinist leads the other musicians. ______
4. The concert hall buzzes with voices. ______
5. Mariachi bands consist of violins, guitars, trumpets, and singers. ______
6. The singers and lead guitarist often practice together. ______
7. Jazz groups perform at the Prithvi Theater in our city. ______
8. A pianist works hard to prepare for a performance. ______

A. **Write the present tense form of the verb in parentheses ( ) that correctly completes each sentence.**

1. Mariachi bands ______________ all over the world. (play)
2. My cousin ______________ everywhere with the band. (go)
3. The trumpet player always ______________ a radio with him. (take)
4. The guitarist in this band also ______________ music. (write)
5. The drummer ______________ the conductor carefully. (watch)
6. My favourite singer ______________ two songs on the Top Ten list. (have)
7. My brother and I ______________ to them every morning. (listen)
8. Jamal and Denise ______________ the city every year. (visit)

# The Faraway Country

*To multiply with a 2-digit factor that requires regrouping, follow these steps.*

1. *Multiply the ones. Regroup if needed.*
   *7 x 3 = 21*

$$\begin{array}{r} {}^{2}\\ 67 \\ \times\ 3 \\ \hline 1 \end{array}$$

2. *Multiply the bottom factor in the ones column with the top factor in the tens column. Add the extra tens.*
   *6 x 3 = 18     18 + 2 = 20*

$$\begin{array}{r} {}^{2}\\ 67 \\ \times\ 3 \\ \hline 201 \end{array}$$

Multiply.

A. 48 x 3 =     24 x 7 =     73 x 4 =

B. 57 x 7 =     63 x 9 =     56 x 3 =

C. 98 x 2 =     64 x 8 =     57 x 8 =     35 x 9 =     23 x 8 =     82 x 6 =

D. 95 x 9 =     77 x 6 =     83 x 9 =     96 x 8 =     28 x 4 =     96 x 5 =

**Switzerland is famous for the magnificent Swiss Alps. Waterfalls are formed by many of the mountain streams. The highest waterfall is Giessbach Falls. To find out how many metres high this waterfall is, add the products in Row A.**

# What's the Topic?

*Every paragraph has a topic sentence that tells the main idea of the paragraph, or what it is about. It usually answers several of these questions:*

**Who? What? Where? When? Why? How?**

*Here are some examples.*

**The doe and her fawn faced many dangers in the forest.**
**We were amazed by our guest's rude behaviour.**
**Baking bread from scratch is really not so difficult, or so I thought.**
**Getting up in the morning is the hardest thing to do.**

*Did these topic sentences grab your attention? A good topic sentence should.*

Here are some topics. Write a topic sentence for each one.

1. **convincing someone to try octopus soup**

2. **an important person in your life**

3. **an embarrassing moment**

4. **the importance of Independence Day**

5. **lunchtime at the school cafeteria**

Now list some topics of your own. Then write a topic sentence for each one.

**Topic #1**

**Topic #2**

**Topic #3**

**Topic sentence #1**

**Topic sentence #2**

**Topic sentence #3**

# Parts of a Paragraph

*A* **paragraph** *is a group of sentences that tells about one main idea. The* **topic sentence** *tells the main idea and is usually the first sentence.* **Supporting sentences** *tell more about the main idea. The* **closing sentence** *of a paragraph often retells the main idea in a different way. Here are the parts for one paragraph.*

*Paragraph Title:* **Starting Over**

*Topic Sentence:* **Today started off badly and only got worse.**

*Supporting Sentences:*

1. **Everyone in my family woke up late this morning.**
2. **I had only 15 minutes to get ready and catch the bus.**
3. **I dressed as fast as I could, grabbed an apple and my backpack, and raced to get to the bus stop on time.**
4. **Fortunately, I just made it.**
5. **Unfortunately, the bus was pulling away when several kids pointed out that I had on two different shoes.**

*Closing Sentence:* **At that moment, I wanted to start the day over.**

*When you write a paragraph, remember these rules:*

- **Indent** *the first line to let readers know that you are beginning a paragraph.*
- **Capitalise** *the first word of each sentence.*
- **Punctuate** *each sentence correctly (? ! . ,).*

Use all the information above to write the paragraph. Be sure to follow the rules.

______________________________
**paragraph title**

______________________________________________________________

______________________________________________________________

______________________________________________________________

______________________________________________________________

______________________________________________________________

______________________________________________________________

______________________________________________________________

# Math's Got It Covered

This soccer player sure has a lot of ground to cover. Just how much exactly? Look at the picture and answer the questions.

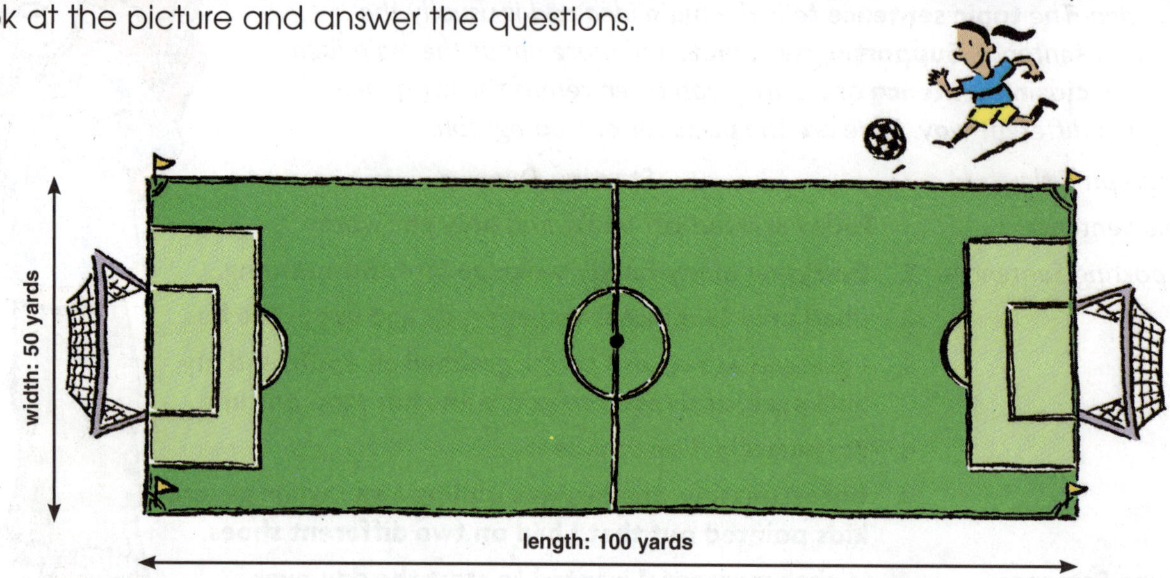


1. a. **What is the length of the field?** **yards** ______ **feet** ______
   b. **What is the width of the field?** **yards** ______ **feet** ______
   c. **What is the perimeter of the field?** **yards** ______ **feet** ______
   d. **What is the area of the field?** **yards** ______ **feet** ______

2. a. **What is the perimeter of half of the field?** **yards** ______ **feet** ______
   b. **What is the area of half of the field?** **yards** ______ **feet** ______

3. **Imagine a field with a length of 130 yards and a width of 75 yards.**
   a. **What is the perimeter of that field?** ________
   b. **What is the area of that field?** ________

### All-Star Math!

Is the perimeter of half the field what you expected? Why or why not?

____________________________________

____________________________________

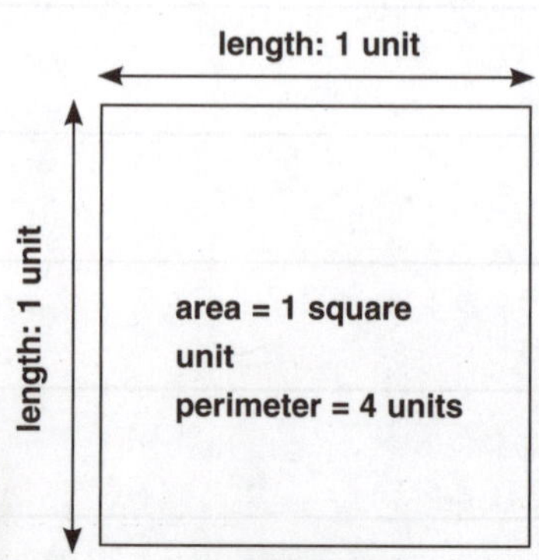


**area = length x width**
**perimeter = sum of the sides**



Scholastic Inc. *Summer Express: Between Grades 4 & 5*

# The Wonderful Whale

*A* ***summary*** *tells the most important parts of a story.*

**For each paragraph, circle the sentence that tells the most important part.**

1. The largest animal that has ever lived is the blue whale. It can grow up to 300 feet long and weigh more than 100 tons. Whales, for the most part, are enormous creatures. However, some kinds only grow to be 10 to 15 feet long.

**The blue whale is the largest animal.**
**Most whales are enormous creatures.**
**Some whales are only 10 to 15 feet long.**

2. Whales look a lot like fish. However, whales differ from fish in many ways. For example, the tail fin of a fish moves up and down; the tail fin of a whale moves sideways. Fish breathe through gills. Whales have lungs and must come to the surface from time to time to breathe. Whales can hold their breath for a very long time. The sperm whale can hold its breath for about an hour.

**Whales and fish do not share similar breathing patterns.**
**Whales can hold their breath for about an hour.**
**Whales might look a lot like fish, but the two are very different.**

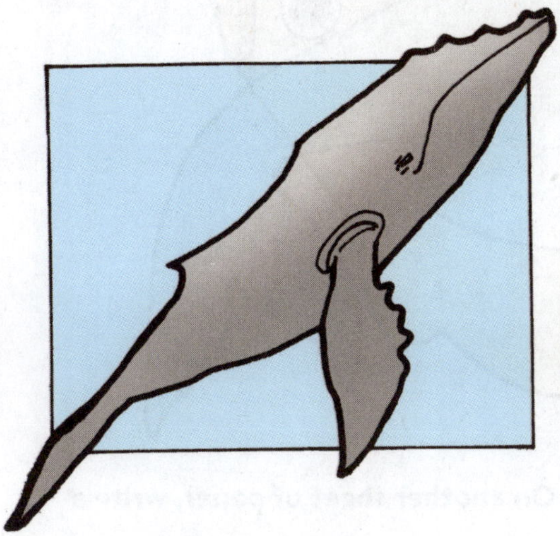

3. Baleen whales have no teeth. Toothed whales have teeth. Baleen whales have hundreds of thin plates in their mouth. They use these plates to strain out food from the water. Their diet consists of tiny plants and animals. Toothed whales eat such foods as other fish, cuttlefish and squid.

**Whales can be divided into two groups—baleen and toothed.**
**Baleen whales have plates in their mouths; toothed whales do not.**
**Toothed whales use their teeth to chew their food.**

4. Whales have a layer of fat called blubber. Blubber keeps them warm. Whales can live off their blubber for a long time if food is scarce. Blubber also helps whales float, as it is lighter than water.

   **Layers of fat are called blubber.**

   **Blubber is very important to whales and has many purposes.**

   **Blubber is what makes whales float.**

5. **Write the main idea of each paragraph to complete a summary about whales.**

   ______________________________________________

   ______________________________________________

   ______________________________________________

   ______________________________________________

   ______________________________________________

6. **Fill in the whale and the fish with the following descriptions. Write the descriptions that are specific to each on the spaces that don't overlap. Write what the two have in common in the shared space.**

   **can hold breath for long time** | **people love to watch**
   **gills** | **tail fin sideways**
   **live in ponds** | **tail fin up and down**
   **live in oceans** | **lungs**

**Read information about another animal. On another sheet of paper, write a summary of the information.**

# Helping Your Child Get Ready: Week 6

These are the skills your child will be working on this week.

**Maths**
- subtracting fractions
- adding money

**Reading**
- making inferences
- comparing and contrasting

**Writing**
- writing topic sentences

**Vocabulary**
- homophones

**Spelling**
- spelling patterns

**Here are some activities you and your child might enjoy.**

**Compound It** Ask your child to list as many compound words as possible that contain the word *house*.

**Compliment Jar** Create a compliment jar. Label a clear plastic jar with the word "Compliments." Invite everyone in your home to write a compliment for another family member on a slip of paper and place it in the jar. Once a week, invite your child to read the compliments aloud to the rest of the family.

**Circle Graph** Have your child make a circle graph showing how he or she spends time in a typical 24-hour period.

**Window Poem** Have your child write a window poem. Have him or her look out a window and write a short poem about what he or she sees.

**Your child might enjoy reading the following books:**

*Harry Potter and the Deathly Hallows*
*by JK Rowling*

*Children of the Enchanted Jungle*
*by Timeri Murari*

*Geronimo Stilton and the Super Chef Contest*
*by Geronimo Stilton*

## _________________________'s Incentive Chart: Week 6

Name Here

This week, I plan to read __________ minutes each day.

CHART YOUR PROGRESS HERE.

| Week 1 | Day 1 | Day 2 | Day 3 | Day 4 | Day 5 |
|---|---|---|---|---|---|
|  I read for... | minutes | minutes | minutes | minutes | minutes |
| Put a sticker to show you completed each day's work. | | | | | |

# Congratulations!

Wow! You did a great job this week!

Place sticker here.

Parent or Caregiver's Signature ______________________________

# A Beastly Puzzle

How many three- and four-letter animal names can you find in this puzzle? Words can be spelled by moving from letter to letter along the lines connecting the circles. For example, you can form the word DOG by starting at the D, moving left to the O and then up to the G. There are six more animals names in the puzzle.

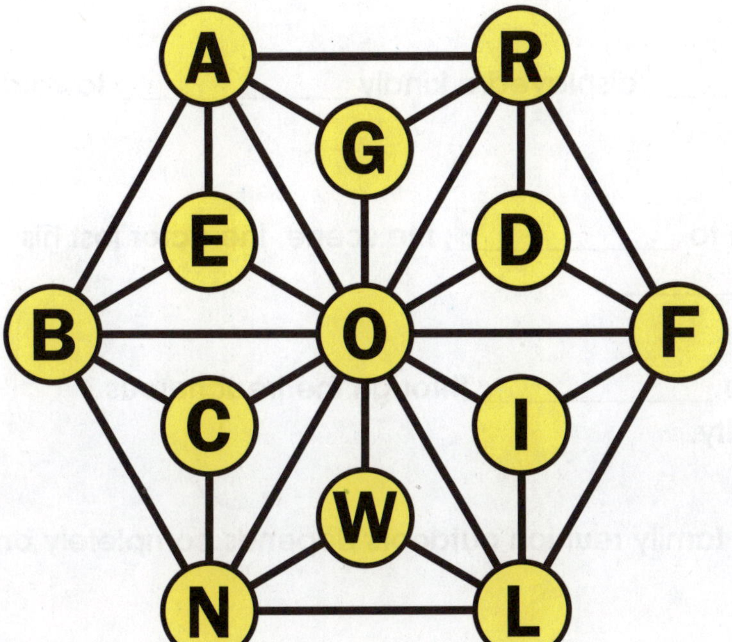

**Bonus:** There are lots of other words in this puzzle that aren't names of animals. Find as many as you can.

# Which One Do You Mean?

*A* ***homophone*** *is a word that sounds just like another word, but it has a different spelling and a different meaning.*

Write the correct homophone in each blank to complete the sentence. Use a dictionary if necessary.

1. **ball, bawl**
   **The toddler started to ____________ when the dog ran off with her ____________.**
2. **manner, manor**
   **The lord and lady of the ____________ displayed a kindly ____________ toward their servants and staff.**
3. **chute, shoot**
   **Just as the cameraman was about to ____________ the scene, the actor lost his balance and slid down the ____________.**
4. **straight, strait**
   **The captain skillfully sailed the ship ____________ through the treacherous ____________ without any difficulty.**
5. **weather, whether**
   **____________ or not we hold the family reunion outdoors depends completely on the ____________ that day.**
6. **least, leased**
   **According to our neighbours, Mr Jenkins ____________ the house across the street for at ____________ two years.**

The homophones are used incorrectly in the sentences below. Cross out each incorrect word. On another sheet of paper, rewrite the sentences with the correct words.

7. **I slipped the bridal over my hoarse's head, took the reign, and lead the animal toward the riding path.**
8. **The air to the thrown proved to be a fare ruler.**
9. **Theirs an extra hangar in the close closet.**
10. **We ordered stake sandwiches on toasted hole wheat bred.**
11. **The boys leaped over the creak and duct behind a bolder, hoping they wood not be scene.**
12. **We needed the doe, aloud it to rise, and baked it for an our and a half.**

# Topic Talk

*Most paragraphs begin with a topic sentence, but it can appear elsewhere in a paragraph. Sometimes a topic sentence is located at the end of a paragraph or even in the middle.*

**A boiling mass of clouds was almost overhead. A bolt of lightning streaked across the darkened sky. Thunder boomed, and it began to rain and hail. We had to find a safe place quickly! There wasn't a moment to spare because early summer storms sometimes turn into tornadoes.**

*Read the paragraph again. This time try the topic sentence elsewhere in the paragraph.*

Read each paragraph. Notice that each one is missing a topic sentence. Think about the supporting sentences. What main idea do you think they support? Write a topic sentence to tell the main idea of each paragraph. Remember that a topic sentence is not always the first sentence of a paragraph.

1. **The days are growing longer. The winter snows are melting as the temperatures rise. Colourful crocuses are popping up here and there. Robins have begun to return north, and creatures are beginning to come out of their winter burrows.**

   ____________

   ________________________________________________

2. ________________________________________________

   **It was fun and easy. Students, parents, and teachers began saving the box tops from all Healthful Foods products. After we collected 100,000 box tops, we mailed them to Healthful Foods headquarters. We earned 50 paise for each box top for a total of ₹50,000. Our school will use the money to buy computers.**

3. **It is just a couple of days to Dhanteras. You know what that means.**

   ________________________________________________

   **This year the festivities will begin with a mela at the colony playground. As always, there will be lights, music, dancing, lots of great food, games, and some new surprises! We look forward to seeing you.**

# Fraction Subtraction

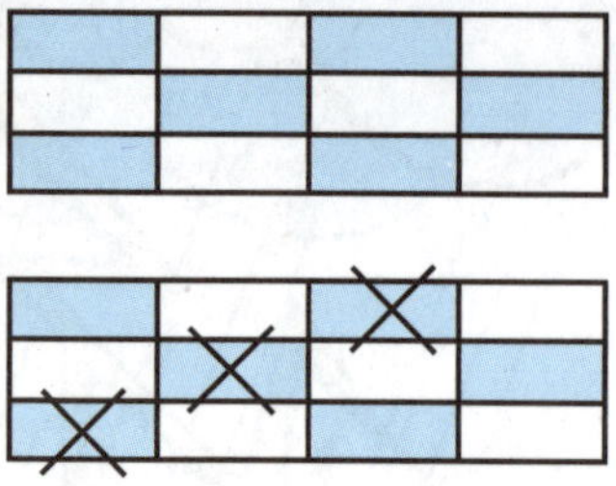

*How many squares are there in all?* **12**

*What fraction of squares are coloured?* $\frac{6}{12}$

*Subtract the fraction of marked-out squares.* $\frac{6}{12} - \frac{3}{12} = \frac{3}{12}$

*What fraction of coloured squares remain unmarked?* $\frac{3}{12} = \frac{1}{4}$

Write out the fraction subtraction problem. Subtract. Reduce to lowest terms.

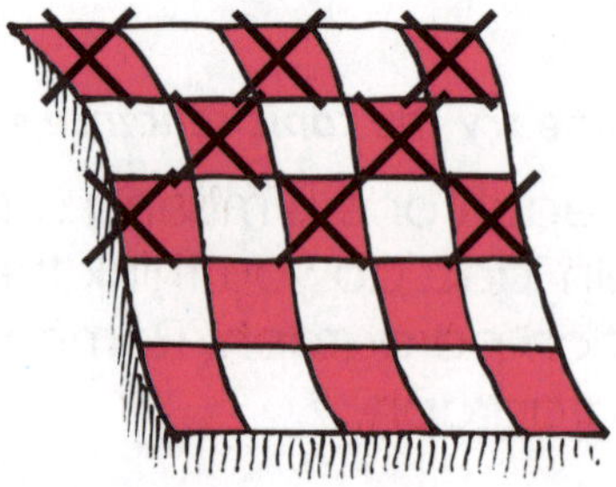

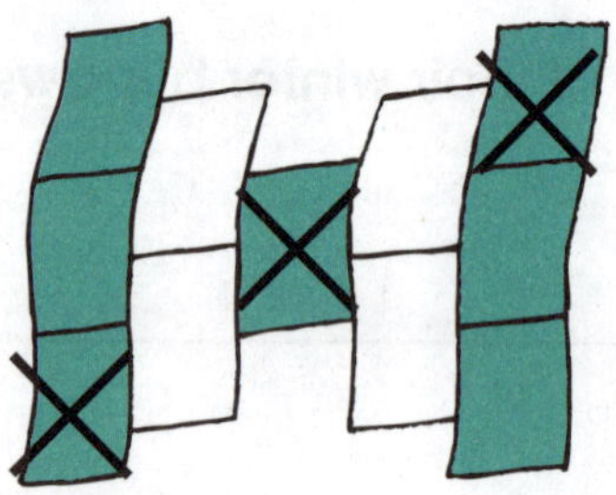

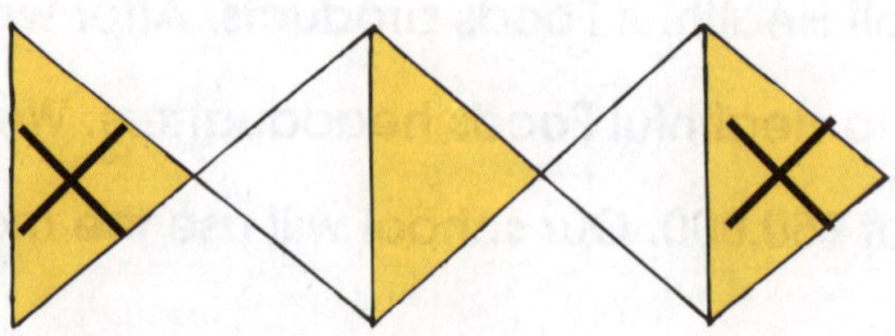

**Jason is travelling to the beach with his grandparents. Jason's grandfather told Jason that when they had travelled 5/8 of the way, they would stop to stretch and get a snack. They have only travelled 3/8 of the way. What fraction of the way must Jason wait before they stop?**

# A Lot of Details

*When you are ready to write a topic sentence, think about the main topic or idea of the paragraph you will be writing and the details you plan to include. Then jot down several possible sentences and choose the best one. Remember that a topic sentence can answer several questions: Who? What? Where? When? Why? How?*

*Tony Hawk*

- *skateboarder*
- *in his forties*
- *turned professional at age 14*
- *has won more skateboarding contests than anyone*
- *made history at Summer X Games in 1999—landed a "900" (a complete somersault done 2 ½ times in midair)*

*Possible topic sentences:* **There is no other skateboarder like Tony Hawk.**
**Tony Hawk is an extraordinary skateboarder.**
**Tony Hawk is the "old man" of skateboarding.**

Here are some topics with details. Write two topic sentences for each one on the lines below.

| 1. **Pet Rocks** | 2. **Komodo Dragon** | 3. **A Great Dessert** |
|---|---|---|
| — fad in the 1970s<br>— idea came from Gary Dahl, a salesman<br>— sold rocks as pets<br>— came with a manual<br>— manual had tips on how to teach a pet rock tricks | — member of monitor family<br>— grows to 10 feet and weighs 136 kg<br>— meat eater<br>— dangerous to humans<br>— largest lizard in the world<br>— long neck and tail, strong legs<br>— found on Komodo Island | — slice a banana<br>— add vanilla ice cream<br>— sprinkle on some walnuts<br>— cover with lots of hot fudge sauce<br>— top with mounds of whipped cream and a cherry |

1. ______________________________

______________________________

2. ______________________________

______________________________

3. ______________________________

______________________________

Remember that the supporting sentences you write support or tell more about the main idea in your topic sentence. Read the paragraph below. Draw one line under the topic sentence. Draw two lines under the supporting sentences. Check (√) the closing sentence.

**Tony Hawk**

**Tony Hawk is an extraordinary skateboarder. He turned professional when he was only 14 years old. Now in his forties, Tony has won more skateboarding contests than anyone else has. He even made history in 1999 by landing a trick called the "900" at the Summer X Games. Tony Hawk may just be the greatest skateboarder in the world.**

Now, review the topics on page 75. Choose one. Then review the details listed about the topic in the box. Next, use the information to write at least three supporting sentences to support the topic sentence you wrote. Include a closing sentence and a title. Write the paragraph below.

**Make a list of topics you would like to write about. Choose one. Then list on a sheet of paper details you know about the topic. Do some research if necessary. Then write a topic sentence and several supporting sentences.**

# Guess the State

Smita, Jai, Garima and Keshav are new in Mrs Desai's class. Each of these students came from one of the following states: Maharashtra, Rajasthan, West Bengal and Kerala. They are taking turns giving the class clues about the state from which they moved. The other children are trying to guess the state from the clues.

**Use the following clues to help you determine which state was the home of each new student. Write each new student's name on the correct state outline below. Label the state in which all the students now live.**

1. **Smita is not from the desert state.**
2. **Garima is not from the south or the east.**
3. **Keshav is not from the south or the west.**
4. **Jai is not from the south or the west.**
5. **Garima and Smita both are from coastal states.**
6. **Jai and Keshav both had lots of Marwari friends in their earlier states.**
7. **Garima's father worked as a script writer for Hindi films.**
8. **Most of Smita's old friends love eating idlis for breakfast.**
9. **Keshav used to live in the colonial capital of thje British Raj.**
10. **Jai used to study in a well-known boarding school, in the city which is home to the dargah of Moinuddin Chishti.**
11. **All four children love their new state. It is located in the northern part of the country. It is famous for chaat and politics. This historic state is also a city which was destroyed and rebuilt several rulers.**

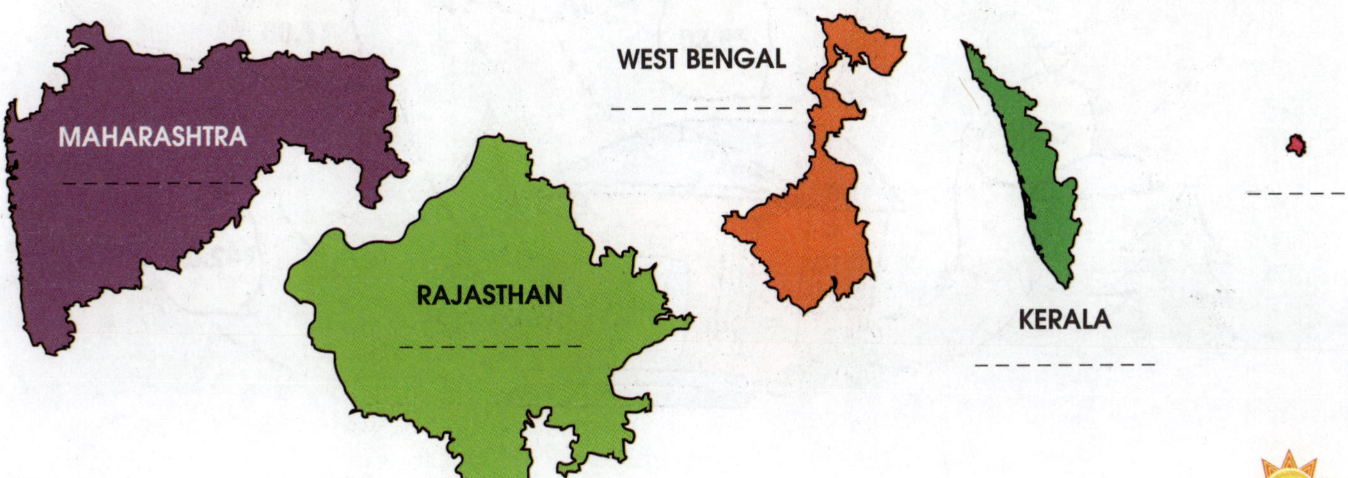

# Greedy Gretchen

Gold! Gold! Gold! Help Greedy Gretchen find the path through the Soyam forest in Tehri from her house to the bank. On which path can she collect the most gold? Draw a line to show that path. On another sheet of paper, explain your answer.

Use with page 80.


# Many Thanks

Giving thanks is a custom among people all around the world. Like the Indian festival of Pongal, celebrated every year in mid January, specially in Tamil Nadu. The festival is a way of showing gratitude to God, the sun, the earth and the cattle for a good harvest. In Korea, people have celebrated a fall holiday called Ch'usok for more than 1,000 years. Families prepare special foods using newly harvested crops. On the holiday itself, Koreans give thanks and remember their ancestors. Later in the day, they enjoy a feast of rice cakes, fresh fruit, and vegetable soup. In India, Pongal also coincides with other thanksgiving-harvest festivals like 'Bhogali Bihu' in Assam, Lohri in Punjab, 'Bhogi' in Andhra Pradesh and 'Makar Sankranti' in the rest of the country. Pongal, which literally means "boiling over" or "overflow", is also the name of a sweet dish made by boiling rice and lentils. This dish is traditionally cooked and consumed on this day, along with the family.

**Write three headings on the diagram. Under each heading, add facts from the passage.**

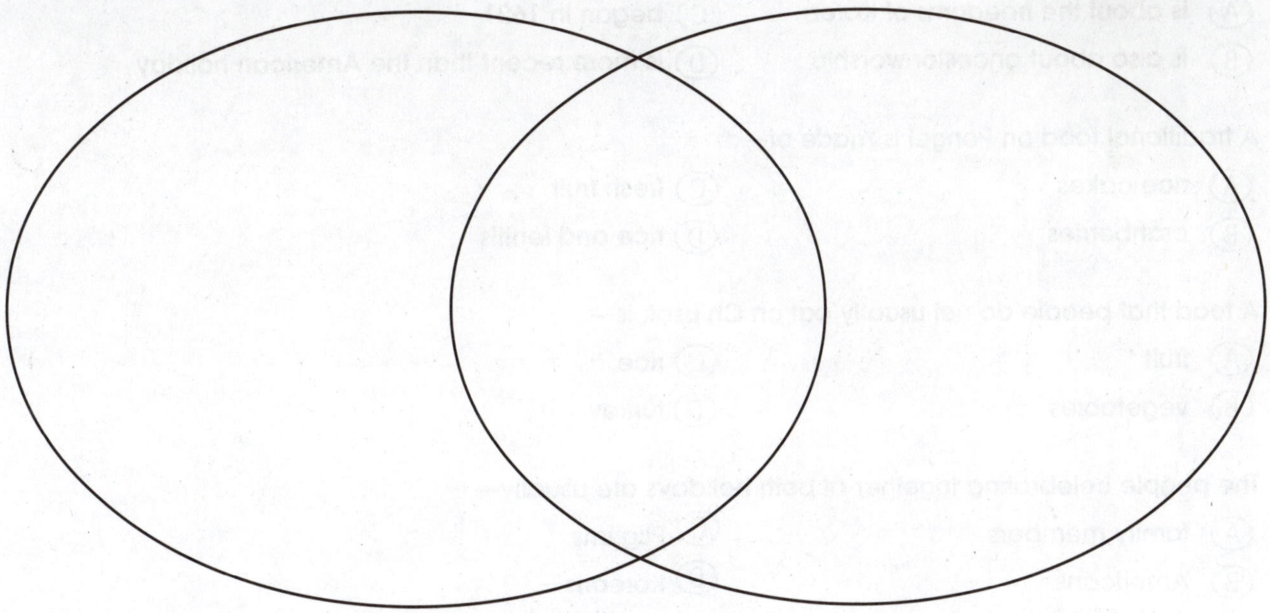

**MORE!** Find out who Sarah Josepha Hall was and why she is known in the U.S. as "the mother of Thanksgiving."

# Testing It Out

Use after completing Many Thanks on page 79.
Fill in the circle of the best answer.

1. The passage compares—
   - Ⓐ Thanksgiving and Ch'usok
   - Ⓑ kinds of memorial services
   - Ⓒ Ch'usok and Pongal
   - Ⓓ Wampanoags and Koreans

2. On both holidays, people—
   - Ⓐ give gifts
   - Ⓑ make rice cakes
   - Ⓒ roast turkeys
   - Ⓓ show gratitude

3. Both holidays are celebrated—
   - Ⓐ in the spring
   - Ⓑ in the fall
   - Ⓒ after the harvest
   - Ⓓ before the harvest

4. The Korean holiday—
   - Ⓐ is about the freedoms of Korea
   - Ⓑ is also about ancestor worship
   - Ⓒ began in 1621
   - Ⓓ is more recent than the American holiday

5. A traditional food on Pongal is made of—
   - Ⓐ rice cakes
   - Ⓑ cranberries
   - Ⓒ fresh fruit
   - Ⓓ rice and lentils

6. A food that people do not usually eat on Ch'usok is—
   - Ⓐ fruit
   - Ⓑ vegetables
   - Ⓒ rice
   - Ⓓ turkey

7. The people celebrating together at both holidays are usually—
   - Ⓐ family members
   - Ⓑ Americans
   - Ⓒ Pilgrims
   - Ⓓ Koreans

8. From this passage you can guess that—
   - Ⓐ Koreans do not eat dessert
   - Ⓑ rice is an important food in Korea
   - Ⓒ all Thanksgivings are the same
   - Ⓓ Indians do not eat rice

# Helping Your Child Get Ready: Week 7

These are the skills your child will be working on this week.

**Maths**
- measurement
- multiplication word problems
- bar graphs

**Reading**
- finding the main idea

**Writing**
- supporting details
- writing a poem
- writing a comparison paragraph

**Vocabulary**
- analogies

**Grammar**
- complete sentences

### Here are some activities you and your child might enjoy.

**Idiom Pictionary** Play idiom pictionary. Have your child choose an idiom, such as "apple of my eye" or "turn over a new leaf" and draw a picture of it for others to guess.

**Timeline** Have your child create a timeline of his or her life. The timeline can start with his or her birth, and include other significant dates such as births of siblings, first tooth and first day of school.

**Comparison Shopping** Collect flyers or newspaper ads from several grocery stores. Give your child a list of items you regularly shop for. Have him or her use the flyers and ads to determine which store has the best deals.

**Plan the Menu** Have your child plan your dinner menu and then help cook the meal. Ask him or her to be sure to think about the food pyramid nutritional guidelines.

### Your child might enjoy reading the following books:

*With Love from the Hills*
*by Ruskin Bond*

*Superfudge*
*by Judy Blume*

*Diary of a Wimpy Kid: Rodrick Rules*
*by Jeff Kinney*

## _____________'s Incentive Chart: Week 7

Name Here

This week, I plan to read __________ minutes each day.

CHART YOUR PROGRESS HERE.

| Week 1 | Day 1 | Day 2 | Day 3 | Day 4 | Day 5 |
|---|---|---|---|---|---|
|  I read for... | minutes | minutes | minutes | minutes | minutes |
| Put a sticker to show you completed each day's work. | | | | | |

# Congratulations!

Wow! You did a great job this week!

Place sticker here.

**Parent or Caregiver's Signature** ______________________________

# All in a Day's Work

Think about how the first pair of words is related. Then write the word that completes the second part of the analogy. Use the words in the box or another word you know that fits.

| conductor | cashier | custodian |
|---|---|---|
| astronaut | professor | paratrooper |
| geologist | architect | archaeologist |
| hairdresser | physician | astronomer |

1. **Spade is to gardener as baton is to ________________.**
2. **Athlete is to team as ________________ is to faculty.**
3. **Lawyer is to courtroom as ________________ is to salon.**
4. **Pattern is to seamstress as blueprint is to ________________.**
5. **Cook is to chef as clean is to ________________.**
6. **Scuba is to diver as parachute is to ________________.**
7. **Mechanic is to garage as ________________ is to space station.**
8. **Screwdriver is to carpenter as stethoscope is to ________________.**
9. **Books are to librarian as rocks are to ________________ .**
10. **Flight attendant is to airplane as ________________ is to supermarket .**
11. **Collector is to taxes as ________________ is to artifacts.**
12. **Lasso is to cowhand as telescope is to ________________.**

**Notice the suffixes that end many of the words for people. Knowing that the suffix -er means "one who" can help you figure out the meaning of a word. List the suffixes on this page. Find out what they mean.**

# Sassy Sentences

*A* ***sentence*** *is a group of words that expresses a complete thought. When you write a sentence, you put your thoughts into words. If the sentence is complete, the meaning is clear. It contains a subject (the naming part) and a predicate (an action or state of being part).*

| *These are sentences.* | *These are not sentences.* |
|---|---|
| **Sally sells seashells at the seashore.** | **Peck of pickled peppers.** |
| **Betty Botter bought a bit of better butter.** | **Flying up a flue.** |

Make complete sentences by adding words to each group of words. Try to create tongue twisters like the sentences above.

1. ________________________ **flips fine flapjacks.**
2. **Sixty slippery seals** ________________________.
3. ________________________ **fed Ted** ____________.
4. **Ruby Rugby's baby brother** ________________________.
5. ________________________ **managing an imaginary magazine.**
6. **Sam's sandwich shop** ________________________.
7. ________________________ **back blue balloons.**
8. ________________________ **pink peacock pompously** ____________.
9. **Pete's pop Pete** ________________________.
10. ________________________ **sawed Mr. Saw's** ____________.
11. **A flea and a fly** ________________________.
12. ________________________ **black-backed bumblebee.**

**Create your own tongue twisters to share with friends. Make sure each one expresses a complete thought.**

# Drizzle with Details

*A good paragraph needs supporting sentences that tell more about the main idea of the topic sentence. Supporting sentences are sometimes called detail sentences. Every detail sentence in a paragraph must relate to the main idea. In the following paragraph, the one supporting sentence that does not relate to the main idea has been underlined.*

**My first day of softball practice was a total disaster! Not only was I ten minutes late, but I also forgot my glove. Then during batting practice, I missed the ball every time I took a swing. <u>I definitely have improved on my catching skills.</u> To make matters even worse, I tripped in the outfield and twisted my ankle. I was definitely not off to a very good start.**

Read the following paragraph. Underline the topic sentence. Then cross out any supporting sentences that do not relate to the main idea.

**Yesterday our science class went on a field trip to a pond. Next month we're going to the ocean. That will be fun. We've been studying the pond as an ecosystem in class. Our teacher wanted us to observe firsthand all the different habitats in and around the pond. She had us keep a checklist of the different kinds of plants and animals in each pond habitat. One of the boys accidentally fell in. He was really embarrassed. Along the water's edge I saw several kinds of plants partly underwater, two salamanders, snails, and water bugs. I observed many different habitats.**

# Measure by Measure

Josie is surrounded by all kinds of measuring tools. But she's not sure which tool does what! Sure, she knows that a ruler measures the length of something. But she doesn't realise that all the other tools around her are used for measuring things too. Try giving Josie a hand.

**JOSIE'S TOOL BOX**

Yardstick • Thermometer
Measuring tape • Clock
Measuring cup • Ruler
Scale • Teaspoon

**Directions:**

Take a look at the list of measuring tools in Josie's Tool Box. Use the list to answer the questions below.

1. What tool could Josie use to measure the weight of a pumpkin? ____________________
2. What tool could Josie use to measure the width of her math book?
   ____________________
3. Josie plans to watch one of her favorite television shows. What tool could help her measure the length of each commercial that appears during that show?
   ____________________
4. Josie has an awful cough. What tool could she use to measure the amount of cough syrup she should take? ____________________
5. If Josie's mom wants to find out Josie's temperature, which tool could she use?
   ____________________
6. Say Josie wanted to make a cake. What tool could she use to measure the milk she needs to put in the cake mix? ____________________
7. What tool could Josie use to measure the height of her brother's tree house?
   ____________________
8. What tool could Josie give her dad to measure the length of their living room?
   ____________________

Choose four of the measuring tools in Josie's Tool Box. Make a list of things you could measure with each of those tools.

Use with page 88.


# Vanishing Act

***Details** in a story provide the reader with information about the main idea and help the reader better understand the story.*

The Bermuda Triangle is also known as the Devil's Triangle because of all the vanishings that take place here. The explanations range from the mundane to the terrifying.

The Triangle is an area of sea with its points at Florida, Bermuda and the Bahamas. However, the Triangle is not one fixed area; different people have given different versions of how far it stretches.

It all began in 1950, with a newspaper article on how several ships and aircraft had gone missing over sea within the Triangle area. These included Flight 19, a group of five bombers on a training mission in December 1945. However, we should mention that disappearances have been going on since the 19th century, with the vanishing of the schooner USS Grampus in 1843.

Even those on land appear to have been affected. In 1969, two keepers of the Great Isaac Lighthouse in the Bahamas disappeared and were never seen again.

The last radio transmissions, just before the ship or aircraft disappeared, range from the intriguing to the frightening. Some have talked of 'danger', others of 'green and white waters'. No transmission has described exactly what was happening, leading to some of the more fanciful speculations.

Early writers about the Triangle said there must be a supernatural cause behind the disappearances. Others, more rational, have said the Triangle covers part of some of the biggest shipping and air lanes in the world, and that the disappearances are nothing abnormal or larger in number than the average expected here.

But some of the aircraft and ships have simply vanished and never been located, which gives an eerie tone to the story. Whatever be the cause, from freak weather to aliens, human error to deliberate acts of destruction by the crew, the Bermuda Triangle is a place that evokes wonder and fear in equal measure.

1. What is the Bermuda Triangle also known as? ______________________________

_____________________________________________

2. Describe the location of the Bermuda Triangle? ______________________________

_____________________________________________

3. When first did the mysterious disappearances in the Bermuda Triangle come to public notice? ______________________________

_____________________________________________

And How? ______________________________

_____________________________________________

4. Since when have the disappearing acts being going on? ______________________________

_____________________________________________

5. Is the danger in the Bermuda Triangle limited to the waters? ______________________________

_____________________________________________

6. What are the kind of last signals received before ships and planes disappeared off the radar after entering the Bermuda Triangle? ______________________________

7. List three theories about the reasons for the vanishing acts. ______________________________

_____________________________________________

_____________________________________________

_____________________________________________

_____________________________________________

8. Write your own theory. ______________________________

_____________________________________________

_____________________________________________.

**Read up more about the mystery surrounding the Bermuda Triangle. On another sheet of paper, write five most amazing facts you read.**

# The Corner Candy Store

*Word problems that suggest equal groups often require multiplication.*

Write a number sentence for each problem. Solve.

A. **Sam bought 4 candy bars at ₹10.25 each. How much did Sam spend altogether?**

B. **Mr Johnson, the store owner, ordered 48 boxes of jawbreakers. Each box contained 392 pieces of candy. How many jawbreakers did Mr Johnson order?**

C. **Carly's mom sent her to the candy store with 29 party bags. She asked Carly to fill each bag with 45 pieces of candy. How many pieces of candy will Carly buy?**

D. **Thirty-five children visited the candy store after school. Each child spent ₹ 57. How much money was spent in all?**

E. **Mr Johnson keeps 37 jars behind the candy counter. Each jar contains 286 pieces of candy. How many pieces of candy are behind the counter altogether?**

F. **Nick bought each of his 6 friends a milk shake. Each milk shake cost ₹62.98. How much did Nick spend in all?**

# Poems Take Shape

A concrete poem is one that's shaped like its subject matter. Here's an example.

## Pizza Pizzaz

Have you even seen a more delicious sight,
Than a pizza dressed up to go out at night?
Thick tomato sauce and mozzarella cheese,
Mushrooms, sausage, more peppers, please!
Onions, olives, choice chicken!
Anything goes, just hold the tiffin!
Top it all off with a sprinkle of spice—
It's looking so good . . .
Hey, who took a slice?

Now it's your turn. In BOX 1, create a short concrete poem about an umbrella. To get inspired, shut your eyes and imagine that you are an umbrella. How does the rain sound? Are you soaked? Are you lonely? When you're finished, use BOX 2 to design a concrete poem in a shape you choose.

BOX 1

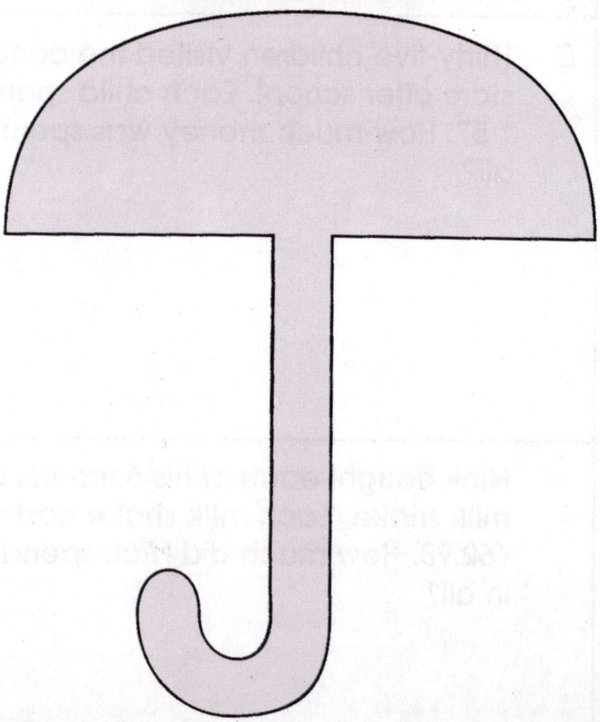

BOX 2

Look for other examples of concrete poems in books of poetry.

# Horseplay

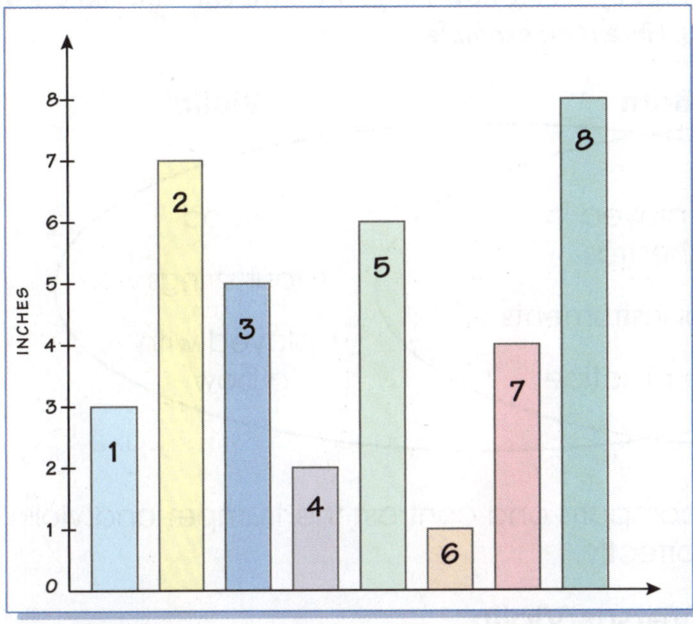


## Why did the horse sneeze?

Answer each question about the graph. Then use the Decoder to solve the riddle by filling in the blanks at the bottom of the page.

1. Which is the tallest bar on the graph? _______
2. Which is the shortest bar on the graph? _______
3. How tall is bar 1? _______
4. How much taller is bar 5 than bar 4? _______
5. How much shorter is bar 4 than bar 2? _______
6. How tall is bar 8? _______
7. Which bar is taller: bar 1 or bar 7? _______
8. Which bar is shorter: bar 2 or bar 3? _______
9. Which bar is twice the size of bar 1? _______
10. How many of bar 4 would equal bar 8? _______

### Decoder

4 bars.................. T
6 inches.............. K
bar 5.................... L
bar 2.................... A
bar 6.................... L
2 inches.............. U
2 bars.................. P
5 inches.............. L
bar 8.................... T
7 inches.............. W
bar 3.................... O
bar 1.................... S
3 inches.............. E
8 inches.............. C
8 bars.................. M
4 inches.............. T
3 bars.................. H
bar 4.................... N
bar 7.................... I

**IT HAD A** ___ ___ ___ ___ ___ ___ "___ ___ ___ ___."

2 7 10 4 9 3 6 8 5 1

# A Musical Lesson

*There are many kinds of paragraphs. When you write a* **comparison paragraph***, you compare by telling how things are similar and contrast by telling how things are different. You can use a Venn diagram to help organise your ideas. Here is an example.*

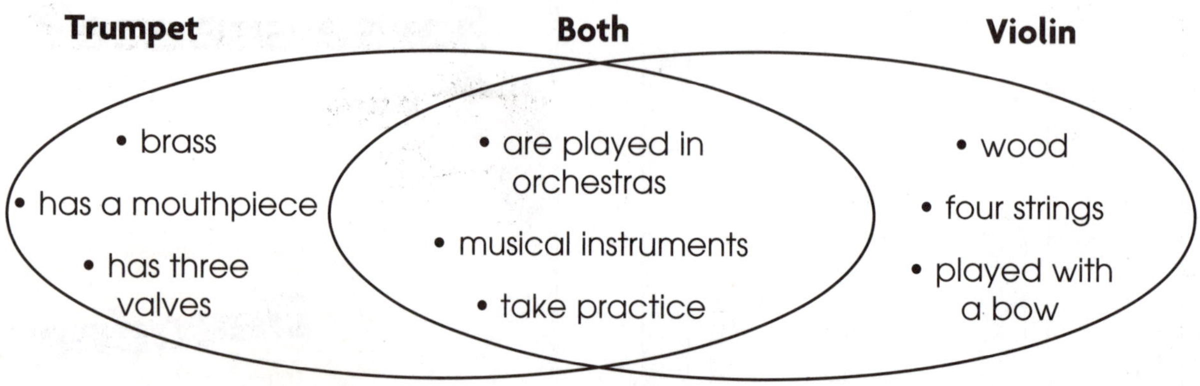


Complete the paragraph using details to compare and contrast the trumpet and violin. Remember to capitalise and punctuate correctly.

## Trumpet Versus Violin

**The trumpet and violin are both musical instruments that are ____________**

**________________________________. However, there are some**

**important differences. The trumpet ________________________________**

________________________________________________

________________________________________________

________________________________________________

**On the other hand, the violin ________________________________**

________________________________________________

________________________________________________

________________________________________________

**Both instruments ________________________________**

________________________________________________

**Make a list on a sheet of paper of things to compare and contrast such as a house and an apartment building, ice skating and skateboarding, or spinach and broccoli. Choose one pair. Make and complete a Venn diagram like the one above. Then write a paragraph to tell how they are similar and different.**

# Helping Your Child Get Ready: Week 8

These are the skills your child will be working on this week.

**Maths**
- multiplying decimals and whole numbers
- division facts

**Reading**
- drawing conclusions

**Writing**
- distinguishing facts and opinions
- writing a persuasive paragraph

**Vocabulary**
- synonyms, antonyms and homophones
- organising words by their meanings

**Grammar**
- parts of speech
- commas and colons
- verb tenses

**Here are some activities you and your child might enjoy.**

**Super Summaries** Writing a summary is often hard for children. To help your child practice this skill, have him or her practice creating one-sentence summaries of favourite books, movies or television shows. To do this, have him or her answer this question in just one sentence: Who did what, when and why? This may take a bit of practice!

**Neat Mnemonics** Mnemonics are a great way to help kids memorise important information. Share the following spelling mnemonics with your child.

There is **a rat** in sep**arat**e.
and
A princi**pal** can be your **pal**.

Encourage your child to make up other mnemonics to help remember tricky spellings.

**Name Acrostic** Invite your child to use his or her name to write a descriptive acrostic poem. For example,

*Awesome*
*Neat*
*Near-sighted*
*Apples*

**Cartography 101** Have your child create a map of your neighbourhood. Take a walk around the area first, and then have him or her decide what symbols and colours to use to represent various buildings and places.

**Your child might enjoy reading the following books:**

*The Mystery of the Secret Hair Oil Formula*
*by Asha Nehemiah*

*Haroun and the Sea of Stories*
*by Salman Rushdie*

______________________ **'s Incentive Chart: Week 8**

Name Here

This week, I plan to read __________ minutes each day.

CHART YOUR PROGRESS HERE.

| Week 1 | Day 1 | Day 2 | Day 3 | Day 4 | Day 5 |
|---|---|---|---|---|---|
|  I read for... | minutes | minutes | minutes | minutes | minutes |
| Put a sticker to show you completed each day's work. | | | | | |

# Congratulations!

Wow! You did a great job this week!

Place sticker here.

**Parent or Caregiver's Signature** ______________________

# Is That a Fact?

*What is the difference between a fact and an opinion? A* ***fact*** *can be checked or proven. An opinion is what someone believes or feels about something. An* ***opinion*** *cannot be proven.*

*Fact* → **Cocoa beans are used to make chocolate.**

*Opinion* → **Chocolate pudding is better than chocolate ice cream.**

Read each sentence. Write *F* next to each fact. Write *O* next to each opinion.

_______ 1. **Everyone in the world thinks chocolate makes the best candy.**

_______ 2. **In Switzerland, the average person eats about 10 kg of chocolate in a year.**

_______ 3. **That means the Swiss eat about 7.5 crore kg of chocolate annually.**

_______ 4. **I think Americans eat more chocolate than that.**

_______ 5. **People also use chocolate to make drinks and to flavour recipes.**

_______ 6. **There's nothing better than a chocolate donut with chocolate glaze.**

Look at the pictures. Then write two facts and two opinions about each snack food. Use clue words such as *think, best, believe, like* and *dislike* to signal an opinion.

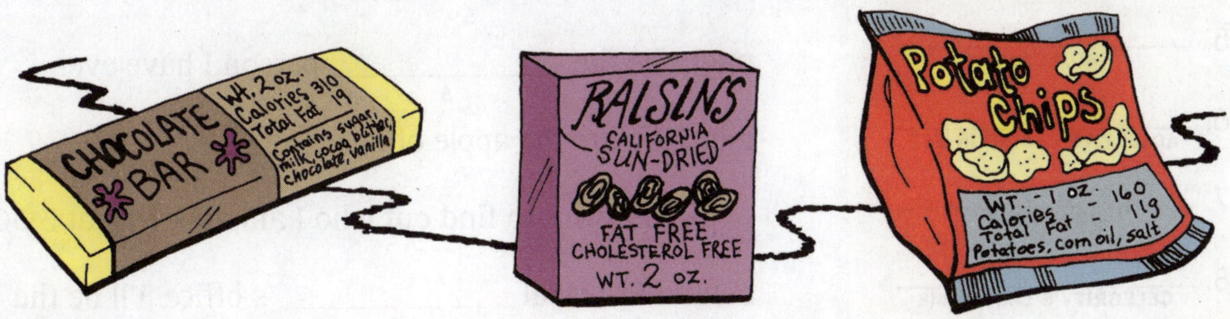


1. **Fact:** ______________________

______________________

______________________

**Opinion:** ______________________

______________________

______________________

2. **Fact:** ______________________

______________________

______________________

**Opinion:** ______________________

______________________

______________________

3. **Fact:** ______________________

______________________

______________________

**Opinion:** ______________________

______________________

______________________

**As you listen to a conversation among your friends about an issue that is important to them, try to identify the facts and opinions you hear and write them down on a sheet of paper. Then ask, "Can this statement be proven?" If the answer is yes, then it is a fact. If not, then it is an opinion. Circle any clue words or phrases that signal opinions.**

# Oh, My Aching Heart!

**Don't read this story yet! Give it to a partner and ask him or her to tell you the parts of speech under the blanks below. You give a word for each part of speech, and your partner writes it in the blank. Then he or she writes the words in the story and reads the story aloud.**

1. ____________ FRIEND'S NAME
2. ____________ PLURAL UNIT OF TIME
3. ____________ ADJECTIVE
4. ____________ VERB ENDING IN *ING*
5. ____________ ADJECTIVE
6. ____________ ADJECTIVE ENDING IN *EST*
7. ____________ BODY PART
8. ____________ CELEBRITY'S LAST NAME
9. ____________ NOUN
10. ____________ PLURAL NOUN
11. ____________ ADVERB
12. ____________ ADJECTIVE
13. ____________ ADJECTIVE ENDING IN *ER*
14. ____________ VERB

Dear ____________ (1),

I have watched you from afar for many ____________ (2) now. I can be silent no longer. The time has come to tell you how I feel. I think you're really smart and ____________ (3). Whenever you are ____________ (4) near me in class, I feel ____________ (5) inside. I think you might be the ____________ (6) person I have ever met. You are the apple of my ____________ (7).

If you want to find out who I am, meet me at 3:30 behind Principal ____________ (8)'s office. I'll be the one wearing the ____________ (9) on my head. Until then, please accept this bunch of ____________ (10) as a sign of my affection.

Yours ____________ (11),

Your ____________ (12) admirer

P.S. It is ____________ (13) to ____________ (14) and lose than never to love at all.

# A Smart Butterfly

*When multiplying with decimals, place the decimal point in the product, counting from right to left, the same number of places as the sum of the decimal places in the factors.*

| | | | |
|---|---|---|---|
| ₹ 6.95<br>x 3 | *The decimal point is 2 places, counting from right to left, in the top factor. There is no decimal point in the bottom factor. 2 + 0 = 2* | ₹ 6.95<br>x 3<br>$ 20.85 | *Place the decimal point 2 places, counting from right to left, in the product.* |

Multiply. Then use the code to answer the riddle below.

| I. | E. | A. | T. | W. | O. |
|---|---|---|---|---|---|
| 2.8<br>x 3 | 26.5<br>x 4 | 32.8<br>x 7 | 20.41<br>x 5 | 0.24<br>x 9 | 0.04<br>x 8 |

| H. | S. | I. | T. | I. | M. |
|---|---|---|---|---|---|
| 3.06<br>x 6 | 300.1<br>x 8 | 24.81<br>x 6 | 24.6<br>x 5 | 41.5<br>x 3 | 0.416<br>x 5 |

| T. | M. | C. | N. | A. | A. |
|---|---|---|---|---|---|
| 45.6<br>x 8 | 48.5<br>x 3 | 4.53<br>x 3 | 3.08<br>x 4 | 3.49<br>x 7 | 6.94<br>x 9 |

**Why did the butterfly learn decimals?**

___ ___    ___ ___ ___    ___
124.5 123.0    2.16 62.46 2,400.08    229.6

___ ___ ___ ___ – ___ ___ ___ ___ ___ ___ ___ ___ ___ .
2.080 0.32 102.5 18.36 – 106.0 145.5 24.43 364.8 148.86 13.59 8.4 62.46 12.32

# Word Wise

Each word below has a synonym, an antonym, and a homophone. See how many you know and can list without referring to the word box at the bottom of the page.

| | Synonym | Antonym | Homophone |
|---|---|---|---|
| 1. **stationary** | | | |
| 2. **taut** | | | |
| 3. **current** | | | |
| 4. **alter** | | | |
| 5. **banned** | | | |
| 6. **bolder** | | | |
| 7. **coarse** | | | |
| 8. **cruel** | | | |
| 9. **sum** | | | |
| 10. **sheer** | | | |
| 11. **birth** | | | |
| 12. **attendance** | | | |

| | | | | | | |
|---|---|---|---|---|---|---|
| moving | shear | currant | kind | hurtful | crewel | stationery |
| berth | smooth | change | braver | permitted | course | difference |
| death | meeker | thick | boulder | band | tight | attendants |
| presence | taught | altar | maintain | outdated | absence | up-to-date |
| loose | some | still | rough | origin | thin | total |
| prohibited | | | | | | |

**Make a chart like the one above for new words. Here are some to get you started.**

**cheap build brake compliment die hire tow foul sweet**

# On the Move

Sameer and Daanish cannot believe that they have to move away from Goa. Goa is so awesome! They can play outside all day long—every day. It is almost always warm and sunny, and all of their friends live there. What will they do without Brendan, Bailey, John, Alexis, and Brian? They will never have such great friends again. Never!

However, Sam and Daanish are very excited for their dad. He has a great new job. The only problem is that the job is in Auli. Daanish was not even sure which state was Auli in. After learning that it is way up in Uttarahand and is a popular ski destination, both boys did get a little excited about playing in the snow. Daanish has always wanted to learn to ski, and Sameer thinks playing ice hockey sounds like fun.

Sameer and Daanish also like the location of Auli. It is between Rudraprayag and Pithoragarh districts and not far from the China border in the north. Neither of the boys has ever visited this part of the country, so they are now looking forward to exploring a new area. If only their friends could come with them! Their parents have promised that they can visit their old friends over spring break and even go to ski resorts. The boys think that moving to Auli will not be so bad after all.

1. **How do** Sameer and Daanish **feel about Goa?** ______________________________

   ______________________________________________________________

2. **Circle how** Sameer and Daanish **feel about leaving their friends.**

   **They are sad.**

   **They do not know what they will do without their good friends.**

   **They know they will make a lot of new friends.**

3. **Circle how the boys feel about moving to Auli.**

   **They think it sounds like a fun, interesting part of the country.**

   **They are excited about visiting their old friends on spring break.**

   **They are disappointed that it is next to Rudraprayag.**

4. **On the map above, label Himachal and make a list of all the states that border it.**

# I'm Convinced!

*In a* **persuasive paragraph,** *you give an opinion about something and try to convince readers to think or feel the way you do. A convincing persuasive paragraph includes*

**— a topic sentence that clearly states your opinion.**
**— reasons that support your opinion.**
**— facts to back up your opinion.**
**— a strong closing sentence that summarises your opinion.**

Pretend you are a world-famous chef who prepares dishes that include edible insects—insects that you can eat. You want to persuade people to include insects in their diet. Here is a topic sentence for a persuasive paragraph.

**Everyone should try cooking with insects.**

Here are some reasons and facts.

- Many insects like mealworms, crickets and weevils are edible.
- People in many cultures around the world eat insects.
- Many insects are low in fat and rich in vitamins.
- Lots of tasty recipes include insects.
- Insects are really quite delicious.

Now put it all together. Write a persuasive paragraph that includes a title and a strong closing sentence. Remember the rules for writing a paragraph.

**Paragraph Title:** ______________________________

**Topic Sentence:** ______________________________

______________________________

______________________________

**Reasons/Facts:** ______________________________

______________________________

______________________________

______________________________

______________________________

______________________________

______________________________

**Closing Sentence:** ______________________________

______________________________

# Television Division

*Each part of a division problem has a name.*

$$\text{divisor} \rightarrow 9\overline{)45} \leftarrow \text{dividend}, \quad 5 \leftarrow \text{quotient}$$

Divide.

**A.**

| | | |
|---|---|---|
| $6\overline{)24}$ | $9\overline{)63}$ | $4\overline{)12}$ |
| $9\overline{)45}$ | $3\overline{)18}$ | $8\overline{)56}$ |
| $8\overline{)64}$ | $8\overline{)40}$ | $9\overline{)72}$ |

**B.**

| | | |
|---|---|---|
| $7\overline{)35}$ | $9\overline{)36}$ | $7\overline{)21}$ |
| $4\overline{)32}$ | $5\overline{)20}$ | $6\overline{)36}$ |
| $3\overline{)9}$ | $7\overline{)56}$ | $9\overline{)81}$ |

**C.**

| | | |
|---|---|---|
| $8\overline{)48}$ | $5\overline{)25}$ | $9\overline{)27}$ |
| $7\overline{)49}$ | $9\overline{)54}$ | $4\overline{)36}$ |
| $5\overline{)15}$ | $7\overline{)63}$ | $7\overline{)28}$ |

**D.**

| | | |
|---|---|---|
| $6\overline{)54}$ | $3\overline{)27}$ | $6\overline{)42}$ |
| $3\overline{)21}$ | $6\overline{)18}$ | $4\overline{)28}$ |
| $5\overline{)30}$ | $5\overline{)40}$ | $7\overline{)42}$ |

**On another sheet of paper, write nine division facts with a quotient of 8.**

# Commas and Colons

**Commas** are used to separate items in a series, to separate parts of dates, to separate parts of names when the last name is written first, and to follow the greeting and closing of letters. **Colons** are used to separate hours and minutes in expressions of time, to introduce a list, and to follow the greeting of a business letter.

A. **Answer the questions, paying careful attention to your use of commas and colons.**

1. Write your name and the names of two classmates as they would appear on an official document. ______________________
______________________
______________________
2. What is your date of birth? ______________________
3. What time does your school begin? ______________ end? ______________

B. **Read each sentence. Add a comma or colon where needed. Write *correct* if the sentence is correct.**

1. Luke Sam and Nick are putting on a play.
2. The play will begin at 800 PM.
3. Yalixa his sister wrote the play.
4. They will perform the play Wednesday and Thursday.
5. Amy can you make the costumes?
6. Like her mom Luisa is a good singer.
7. Our flag is red white and blue.
8. Michael plays baseball and soccer.
9. Nathan will visit on March 28 2004.
10. We are always happy when he comes but sad when he leaves.

# Inside Information

Look at the items in column A of the chart below. Every one of them is commonly found *inside* one item in column B. Match the appropriate pairs and write your answers on the blanks below. There is only one correct letter match for each numbered item. We've done the first one for you.

| COLUMN A | COLUMN B | CORRECT MATCH |
|---|---|---|
| 1. butter | a. balloon | 1. e |
| 2. coin | b. pantry | |
| 3. pupil | c. vault | |
| 4. pig | d. shed | |
| 5. helium | e. refrigerator | |
| 6. cereal | f. sty | |
| 7. assets | g. fountain | |
| 8. rake | h. eye | |
| 9. license | i. bottle | |
| 10. arrow | j. mirror | |
| 11. battery | k. flashlight | |
| 12. mercury | l. quiver | |
| 13. reflection | m. thermometer | |
| 14. lint | n. wallet | |
| 15. message | o. dryer | |

## YOUR TURN

Think of five more items commonly found inside another item, as in the chart above. Mix them up and see if someone in your family can pair them together correctly.

# Grammar Cop

## and the Case of the Emperor's New Clothes

The emperor doesn't know if he's coming or going! He doesn't know what he has done, what he is doing now, and what he will do later. Can you help Grammar Cop choose the right tense?

Decide whether each underlined verb is in the past, present or future tense. Write it in the blank.

_______________ 1. There will be a big parade next week.

_______________ 2. I have nothing to wear.

_______________ 3. I asked the tailors to make me a new cloak.

_______________ 4. They promised to make the best cloak the villagers had ever seen.

_______________ 5. The tailors are working day and night cutting and sewing.

_______________ 6. The cloak is finished!

_______________ 7. I tried it on, and something was very strange . . . .

_______________ 8. But the tailors assured me that the townspeople will be amazed.

_______________ 9. After the parade, all the people said they had never seen anything like my new cloak.

_______________ 10. I tried to find the tailors to thank them, but they had left town.

**Remember these basic laws of tenses:**

- **Past**
  The past tense of a verb tells that something already happened. (Example: I **walked** to school this morning.)
- **Present**
  The present tense of a verb tells that something is happening now. (Example: It **is raining** today.)
- **Future**
  The future tense of a verb tells that something will happen in the future. (Example: Tomorrow I **will play** soccer.)

# Helping Your Child Get Ready: Week 9

These are the skills your child will be working on this week.

**Maths**

- division with remainders
- division with decimals
- changing decimals to fractions

**Reading**

- main ideas and supporting details

**Writing**

- writing an expository paragraph
- using exact verbs

**Vocabulary**

- syllabication

**Grammar**

- proofreading
- dialogue and quotation marks

**Here are some activities you and your child might enjoy.**

**20 Questions** The game of 20 Questions is a great way to build thinking skills. Choose a category (such as animals). Think of one animal. Tell your child he or she can ask only "yes" or "no" questions to determine what animal you're thinking of. Once he or she gets the hang of it, take turns asking questions.

**Local Historians** Have your child research the history of your community. Have him or her find out the name of the Indians who lived in the area, the first Europeans to arrive, the oldest house or building, and the origin of your community's name.

**Numbers That Name You** There are lots of numbers that label, count, measure or order information about a person. For example, everyone has a birthday and an address. Ask your child to think about all the numbers that relate to him or her and list them on a sheet of paper.

**Make a Word** Play this simple word game. Have your child see how many words he or she can make from the letters in the word *Washington.*

**Your child might enjoy reading the following books:**

*The Girl Mechanic of Wanzhou*
*by Marjorie Sayer*

*Matilda*
*by Roald Dahl*

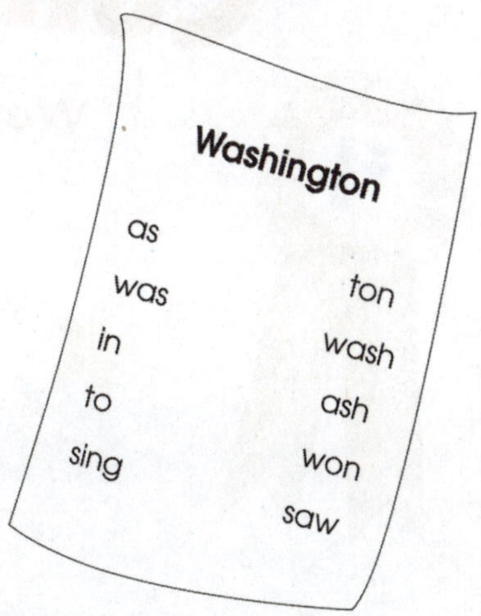

_______________________'s Incentive Chart: Week 9

Name Here

This week, I plan to read __________ minutes each day.

CHART YOUR PROGRESS HERE.

| Week 1 | Day 1 | Day 2 | Day 3 | Day 4 | Day 5 |
|---|---|---|---|---|---|
|  I read for... | minutes | minutes | minutes | minutes | minutes |
| Put a sticker to show you completed each day's work. | | | | | |

# Congratulations!

Wow! You did a great job this week!

Place sticker here.

**Parent or Caregiver's Signature** ______________________________

# Honeycomb

Solve the problems. If the answer has a remainder between 1 and 4, colour the shape yellow. If the answer has a remainder between 5 and 8, colour the shape blue. Finish the design by colouring the other shapes with the colours of your choice.

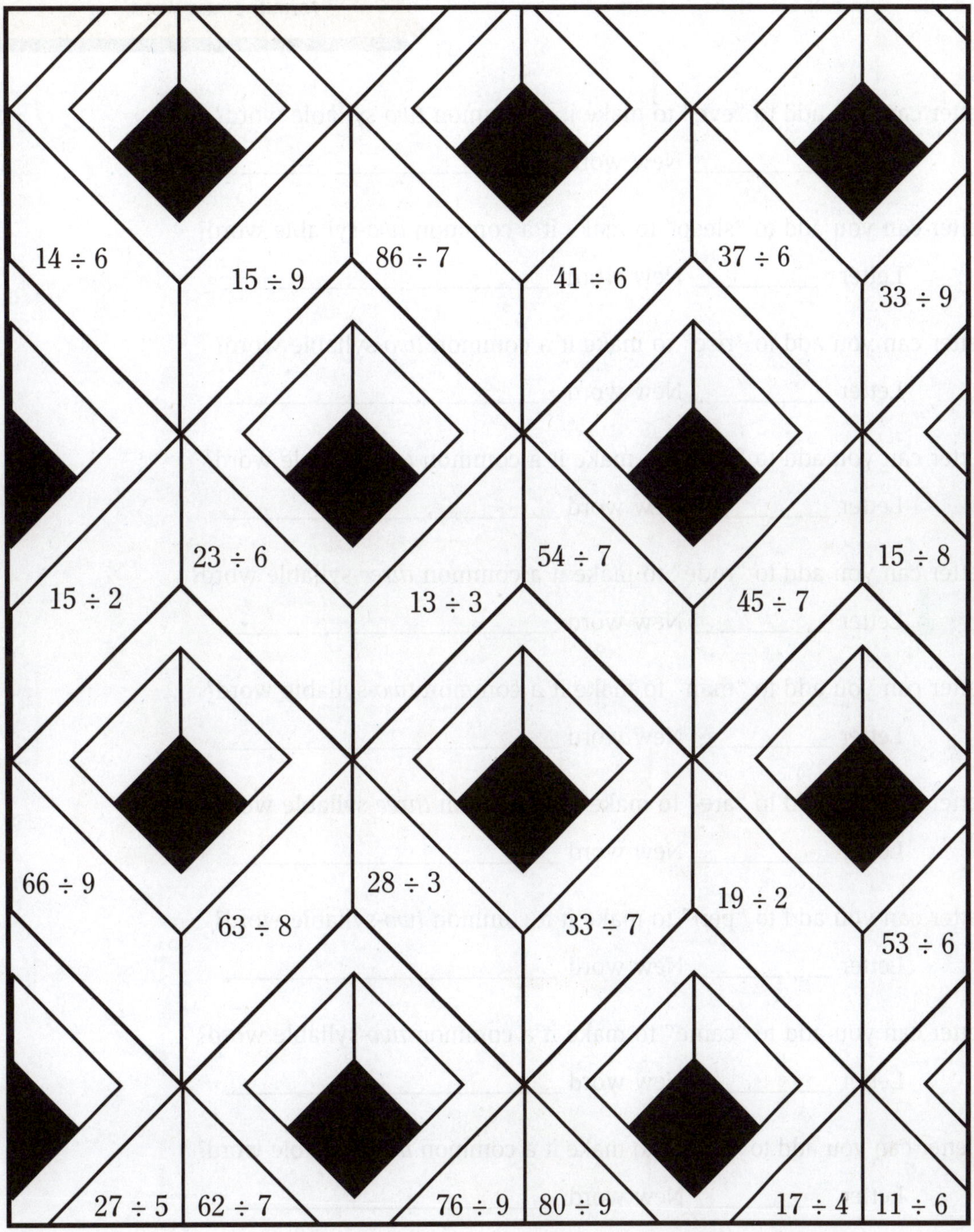

# Syllable Wizardry

How good are you at building words and figuring out how many syllables they have? Answer these tricky and fun questions about words to find out. Some questions may have more than one answer. Write your answers in the blanks.

**TIPS**
- No answers are proper nouns.
- No answers are foreign words.
- Do not rearrange or subtract any letters from the given word to form the new word.

1. What letter can you add to "eve" to make it a common *two*-syllable word?

   Letter __________ New word ______________________

2. What letter can you add to "sleep" to make it a common *two*-syllable word?

   Letter __________ New word ______________________

3. What letter can you add to "rise" to make it a common *two*-syllable word?

   Letter __________ New word ______________________

4. What letter can you add to "rode" to make it a common *two*-syllable word?

   Letter __________ New word ______________________

5. What letter can you add to "rode" to make it a common *three*-syllable word?

   Letter __________ New word ______________________

6. What letter can you add to "man" to make it a common *two*-syllable word?

   Letter __________ New word ______________________

7. What letter can you add to "are" to make it a common *three*-syllable word?

   Letter __________ New word ______________________

8. What letter can you add to "pen" to make it a common *two*-syllable word?

   Letter __________ New word ______________________

9. What letter can you add to "came" to make it a common *two*-syllable word?

   Letter __________ New word ______________________

10. What letter can you add to "came" to make it a common *three*-syllable word?

    Letter __________ New word ______________________

# Step by Step

*When you write an **expository paragraph**, you give facts and information, explain ideas or give directions. An expository paragraph can also include opinions. Here are some topic ideas for an expository paragraph.*

**Explain how to play the flute.**
**Tell why you do not like brussels sprouts.**
**Give facts about yourself.**
**Explain how to bathe a dog.**
**Tell what skills you need to skateboard.**
**Give the facts about your favourite band.**

*Here is an example of an expository paragraph. It explains how to fry an egg.*

**Frying an egg is not all that difficult. After melting a little bit of butter in a frying pan, just crack the eggshell along the rim of the pan and let the egg drop into the pan. Do it gently so the yolk does not break. Let the egg fry over low heat for about a minute or so. That is all it takes.**

Complete the following topics for expository paragraphs with your own ideas.

| **Explain how to** | **Give facts about** | **Tell why** |
|---|---|---|
| ______ | ______ | ______ |
| ______ | ______ | ______ |
| ______ | ______ | |

Use the form below to develop one of your ideas for an expository paragraph.

**Paragraph Title:** ______

**Topic Sentence:** ______

______

**Details/Facts/Steps:** ______

______

______

______

______

**Closing Sentence:** ______

______

Now, use the plan above to write a paragraph on a sheet of paper. If you are giving directions for doing or making something, include words such as *first, next, after that,* and *finally* to make the steps clear for your readers.

# Action Alert

*When you write, think about the verbs that you choose to express action in your sentences. Are they as exact as they can be? Do they tell your readers exactly what you want to say?*

*The child* ***broke*** *the plastic toy.*
*The child* ***smashed*** *the plastic toy.*
*The child* ***cracked*** *the plastic toy.*

*Each verb creates a different picture of what happened.*

Read each sentence. Underline the verb. Then rewrite each sentence using a more exact verb. You may want to use a thesaurus.

1. **Three young hikers went up the steep hill.**

   ______________________________________________

2. **A lone runner ran around the track.**

   ______________________________________________

3. **The wind blew through the treetops.**

   ______________________________________________

4. **The janitor cleaned the scuff marks off the floor.**

   ______________________________________________

5. **The audience laughed at the hilarious scene.**

   ______________________________________________

6. **The diners ate the delicious meal.**

   ______________________________________________

7. **The young tourists liked the castle most of all.**

   ______________________________________________

8. **The children slept for about an hour.**

   ______________________________________________

9. **The biologist looked at the unusual specimen.**

   ______________________________________________

**Here are some commonly used verbs: make, tell, say, speak, ride. On a sheet of paper, list as many exact verbs as you can think of for each one. Use a thesaurus for additional words. Then write several sentences using the exact words on your list.**

# Dialogue and Quotations

**Quotation marks** are used to show the beginning and end of someone's exact words. An **indirect quotation** is a summary of what someone has written or said. Quotation marks are not used in indirect quotes.

A. **In each sentence, underline the words that the speaker or speakers actually said. Then add quotation marks where they belong.**

1. Can't we stay up just five more minutes? the children begged.
2. Kate replied, That's another story.
3. What's for lunch? Bob asked.
4. I am so excited! Betsy cried.

B. **The following dialogue is missing commas, question marks and other necessary punctuation. Write the correct punctuation on each line.**

1. Poissant said_ "I remember once when Duke Ellington stayed at my house_"
2. "Was Duke Ellington famous_" Punkin asked_
3. "He sure was_" Miss Ida exclaimed_
4. "I not only met him_" Poissant explained_ "but I was sitting in the parlour when he sat down at the piano and started to play_"

C. **All the punctuation, including quotation marks, is missing from this dialogue. Write the missing punctuation marks on the lines.**

1. _Duke's playing sure heated up that little room__ exclaimed Poissant_
2. _Did any other famous people stay at your house__ asked Freda_
3. _No__ said Poissant__but Lena Horne once stayed at Miss Jackson's house__
4. Then he added_ _However_ that is a story for another day__

# Ride the Wave of Decimal Division

*Sometimes zeros are needed in the quotient. When dividing decimals by a whole number, follow these steps.*

| Step 1 | Step 2 | Step 3 | Step 4 |
|---|---|---|---|
| $\begin{array}{r} 2\phantom{.08} \\ 27\overline{)55.08} \\ -54\phantom{.08} \\ \hline 1\phantom{.08} \end{array}$ | $\begin{array}{r} 2.\phantom{08} \\ 27\overline{)55.08} \\ -54\phantom{.08} \\ \hline 1\phantom{.08} \end{array}$ | $\begin{array}{r} 2.0\phantom{8} \\ 27\overline{)55.08} \\ -54\phantom{.08} \\ \hline 10\ (< 27) \end{array}$ | $\begin{array}{r} 2.04 \\ 27\overline{)55.08} \\ -54\phantom{.08} \\ \hline 108 \\ -108 \\ \hline 0 \end{array}$ |
| *1. Divide the whole number.* | *2. Place the decimal point in the quotient.* | *3. Bring down the 0. Since it is still < 27, place a zero in the quotient.* | *4. Bring down the 8. Divide into 108.* |

Divide. Then write the letter for each quotient from least to greatest on the lines below to learn where the 1958 megatsunami occurred.

**B.** $62\overline{)126.48}$

**L.** $13\overline{)3.12}$

**Y.** $41\overline{)102.50}$

**A.** $17\overline{)51.85}$

**A.** $13\overline{)62.4}$

**K.** $14\overline{)84.14}$

**I.** $51\overline{)18.36}$

**S.** $17\overline{)86.02}$

**A.** $39\overline{)81.12}$

**U.** $16\overline{)11.04}$

**T.** $32\overline{)18.56}$

**L.** $21\overline{)64.89}$

**A.** $44\overline{)46.64}$

**Y.** $51\overline{)53.856}$

**A.** $31\overline{)188.17}$

**The wave occurred in** ____ ____ ____ ____ ____ ____

____ ____ ____ **in** ____ ____ ____ ____ ____ ____. **It reached 1,720 feet.**

# Proofing Pays

*Capitalisation and end punctuation help show where one sentence ends and the next one begins. Whenever you write, proofread to make sure each sentence begins with a capital letter and ends correctly. Here's an example of how to mark the letters that should be capitalised.*

**have you ever heard of a Goliath birdeater? it is the world's largest spider. this giant tarantula can grow to 11 inches in length and weigh about 170 gram. now that's a big spider! although it is called a birdeater, it usually eats small reptiles and insects. these spiders are mostly found in rain forests.**

Read the passage below. It is about another amazing animal, but it is not so easy to read because the writer forgot to add end punctuation and to use capital letters at the beginning of sentences. Proofread the passage. Mark the letters that should be capitals with the capital letter symbol. Put the correct punctuation marks at the ends of sentences. Then reread the passage.

**think about the fastest car you've ever seen in the Indianapolis 500 race that's about how fast a peregrine falcon dives it actually reaches speeds up to 281 km an hour that's incredibly fast peregrine falcons are also very powerful birds did you know that they can catch and kill their prey in the air using their sharp claws what's really amazing is that peregrine falcons live in both the country and in the city keep on the lookout if you're ever in New York City believe it or not, it is home to a very large population of falcons**

**What do you know about the bee hummingbird, atlas moth, or capybara? Choose one, do some research, and write several sentences about it on a sheet of paper. Then proofread your writing. Does every sentence begin and end correctly? Are all the words spelled correctly?**

# Triangular Patterns

*To change a decimal to a fraction, use the greatest common factor to reduce to lowest terms.*

$0.8 = \frac{8 \div 2}{10 \div 2} = \frac{4}{5}$ $\quad 0.40 = \frac{40 \div 20}{100 \div 20} = \frac{2}{5}$ $\quad 0.250 = \frac{250 \div 250}{1{,}000 \div 250} = \frac{1}{4}$

Using a ruler, draw a line to match each decimal with its fraction.

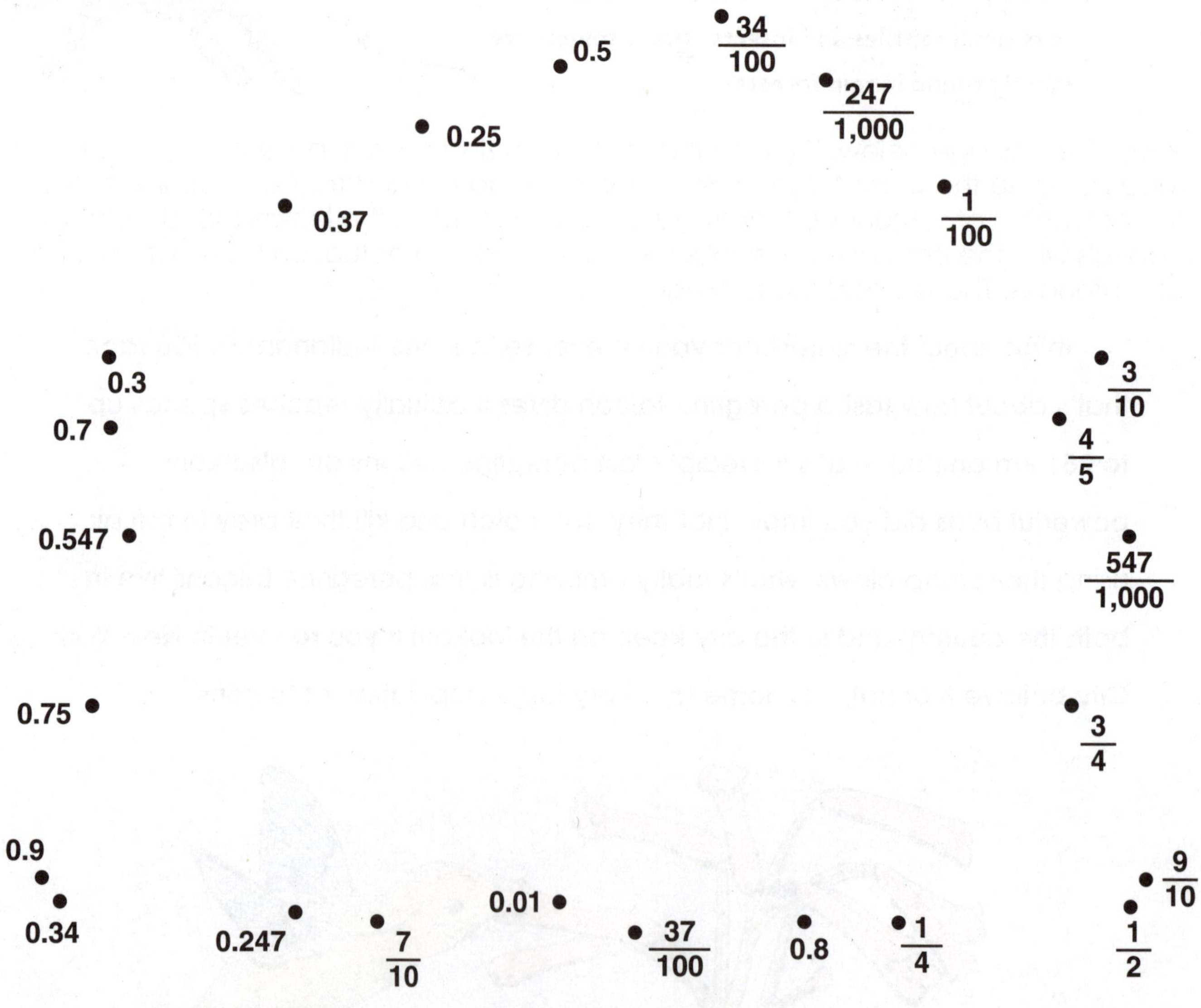


**See how many triangles you can find in the diagram.**

# Eating in Egypt

Suppose you lived thousands of years ago in Ancient Egypt. What would you have eaten? Like all Ancient Egyptians, you would eat bread with every meal. Garlic bread, raisin bread, and nutbread were three favourites. Egyptians also ate a lot of fruit including figs, dates and pomegranates. Vegetables were also part of their diet. Lettuce, beans, onions, cucumbers and leeks were all popular. How do you think you'd like your Egyptian meal?

**Write the topic and three subtopics on the web. Complete the web by writing details for each subtopic.**

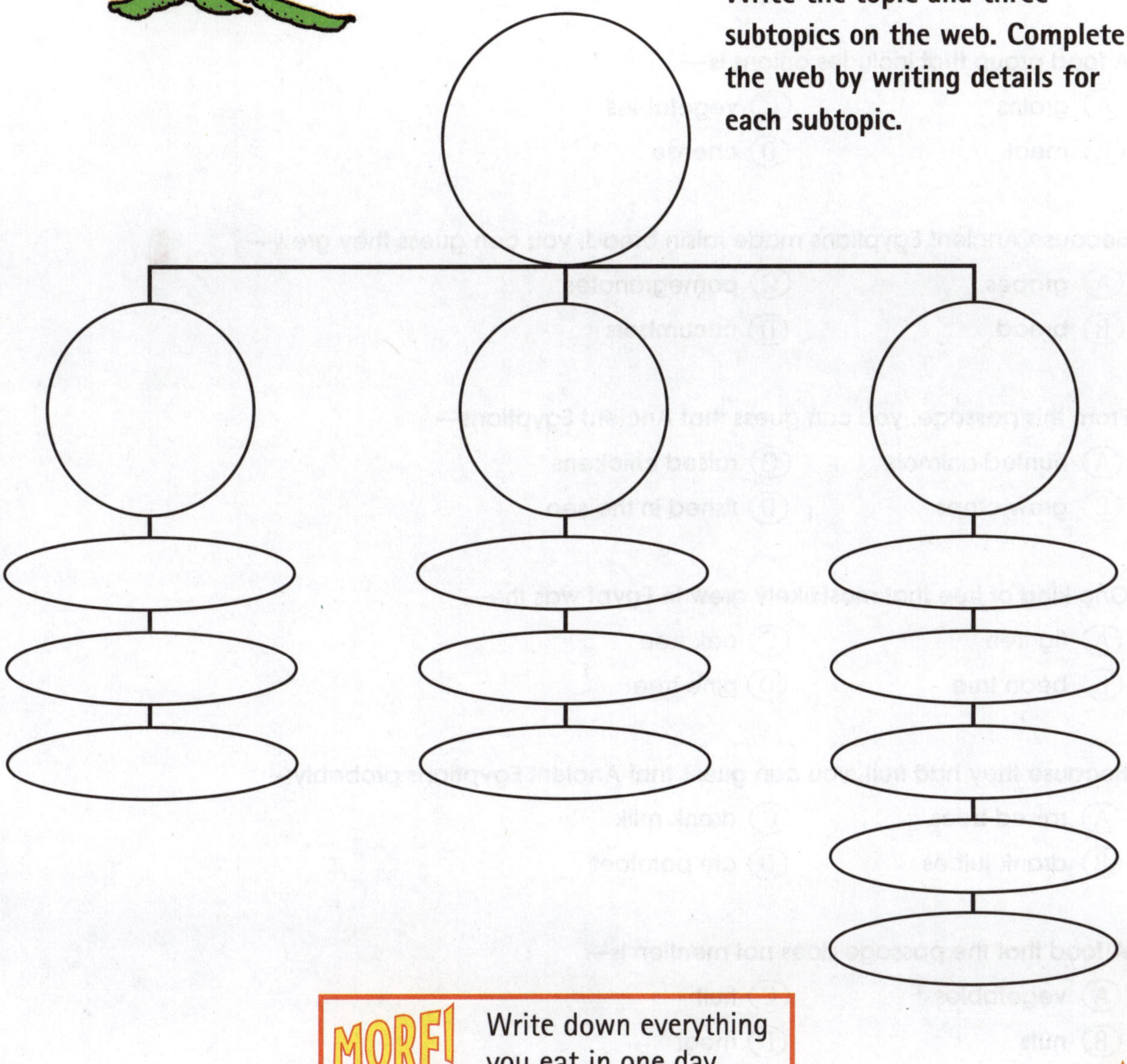

MORE! Write down everything you eat in one day.

Use with page 115.



# Testing It Out

Use after completing Eating in Egypt on page 115.

Fill in the circle of the best answer.

1. **One kind of food that Ancient Egyptians ate at every meal was—**
   - Ⓐ **lettuce**
   - Ⓑ **figs**
   - Ⓒ **bread**
   - Ⓓ **eggs**

2. **Ancient Egyptians often ate fruit called—**
   - Ⓐ **leeks**
   - Ⓑ **beans**
   - Ⓒ **apples**
   - Ⓓ **dates**

3. **A food group that includes onions is—**
   - Ⓐ **grains**
   - Ⓑ **meat**
   - Ⓒ **vegetables**
   - Ⓓ **cheese**

4. **Because Ancient Egyptians made raisin bread, you can guess they grew—**
   - Ⓐ **grapes**
   - Ⓑ **bread**
   - Ⓒ **pomegranates**
   - Ⓓ **cucumbers**

5. **From this passage, you can guess that Ancient Egyptians—**
   - Ⓐ **hunted animals**
   - Ⓑ **grew crops**
   - Ⓒ **raised chickens**
   - Ⓓ **fished in the sea**

6. **One kind of tree that most likely grew in Egypt was the—**
   - Ⓐ **fig tree**
   - Ⓑ **bean tree**
   - Ⓒ **oak tree**
   - Ⓓ **pine tree**

7. **Because they had fruit, you can guess that Ancient Egyptians probably—**
   - Ⓐ **raised bees**
   - Ⓑ **drank juices**
   - Ⓒ **drank milk**
   - Ⓓ **ate potatoes**

8. **A food that the passage does not mention is—**
   - Ⓐ **vegetables**
   - Ⓑ **nuts**
   - Ⓒ **fruit**
   - Ⓓ **meat**

# Helping Your Child Get Ready: Week 10

These are the skills your child will be working on this week.

**Math**

- equivalent fractions
- plotting coordinates
- decimals, fractions, and percents

**Reading**

- determining cause and effect
- standardized reading test practice

**Writing**

- proofreading

**Vocabulary**

- analogies

**Grammar**

- possessives
- commas

**Here are some activities you and your child might enjoy.**

**Create a Moon Calendar** Have your child track the moon's changes for a month. Get or make a calendar for the month that has large boxes. Each night, go outside with your child to look at the moon, and then have him or her draw its shape in that day's box.

**Listen Up** Help your child build listening and memorising skills with this activity. Have him or her listen carefully as you read and reread the list of the five rivers of Punjab below. Then ask your child to repeat it back to you in the same order.

Beas, Chenab, Jhelum, Ravi, Sutlej

**Riddle Me This** Show your child how to make up number riddles. Read the following riddle to your child as a model:

> I am an even number.
> I am the number of outs made in a full,
> 9-inning baseball game.
> I am the product of 6 times 3 times 3.

Once he or she gets the hang of it, have your child create riddles for you to answer.

**Pet Autobiography** Suggest that your child write the story of your pet's (or an imaginary pet's) life. The story should be an autobiography—that is, told from the pet's point of view!

**Your child might enjoy reading the following books:**

*The Mudskipper*
*By Ovidia Yu*

*Wisha Wozzawriter*
*by Payal Kapadia*

*Wonder*
*by RJ Palacio*

## _______________'s Incentive Chart: Week 10

Name Here

This week, I plan to read __________ minutes each day.

CHART YOUR PROGRESS HERE.

| Week 1 | Day 1 | Day 2 | Day 3 | Day 4 | Day 5 |
|---|---|---|---|---|---|
|  I read for... | minutes | minutes | minutes | minutes | minutes |
| Put a sticker to show you completed each day's work. | | | | | |

# Congratulations!

Wow! You did a great job this week!

Place sticker here.

Parent or Caregiver's Signature ______________________________

# Maze

Find the path to the end by passing only through spaces containing words in **bold** that are correctly spelled. The shortest path will take you through 15 spaces with correct spellings.

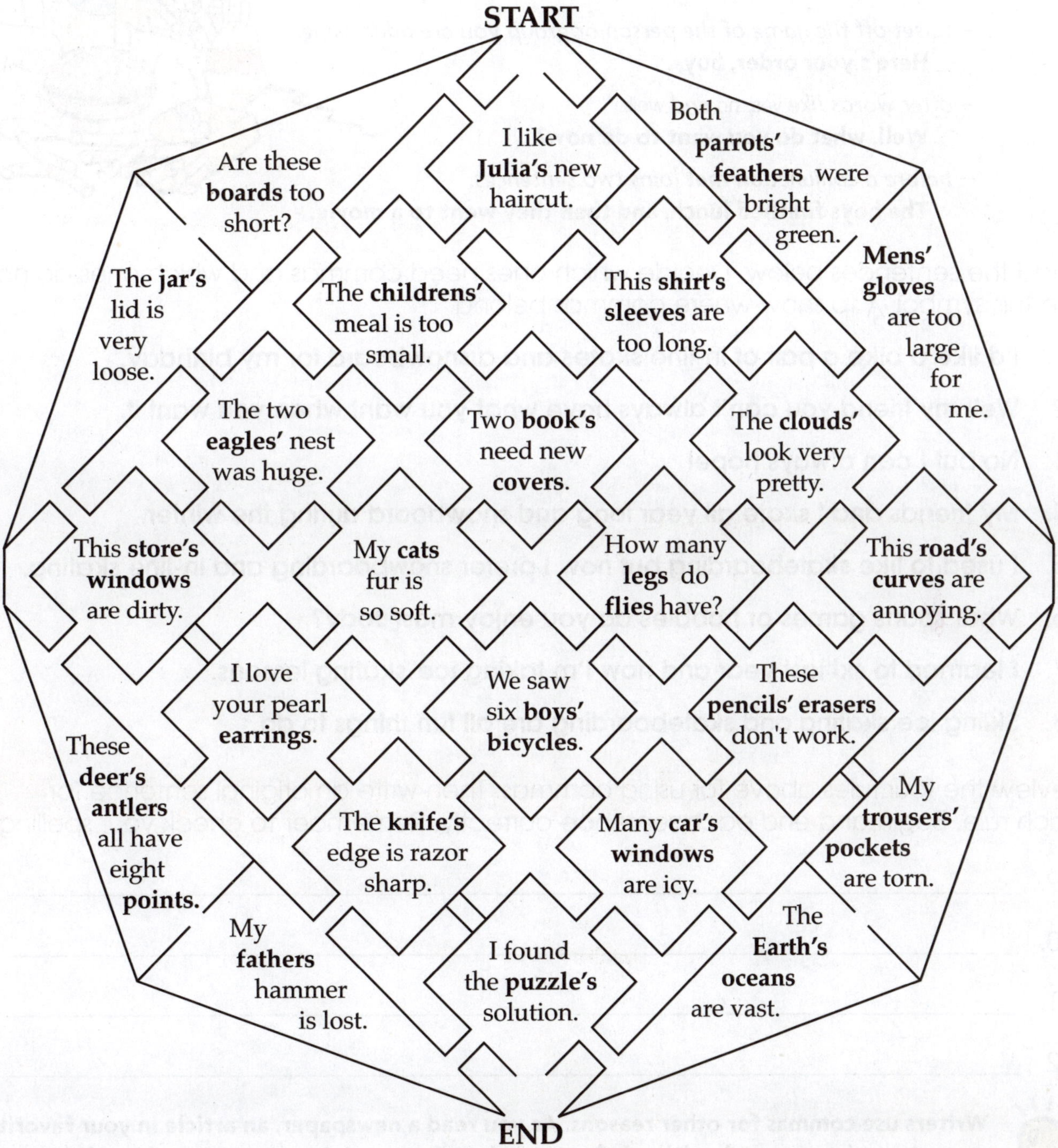

# Comma Capers

*You know that you must use commas in a series of three or more items.*

**Max, Sam and Alex ordered burgers, fries, and milkshakes for lunch.**

*Here are some additional rules you need to know about commas.*
*Use commas*

— *to set off the name of the person or group you are addressing.*

**Here's your order, boys.**

— *after words like* yes, no *and* well.

**Well, what do you want to do now?**

— *before a conjunction that joins two sentences.*

**The boys finished lunch, and then they went to a movie.**

Read the sentences below. Decide which ones need commas and which ones do not. Use this symbol ‸, to show where commas belong.

1. **I'd like a bike a pair of in-line skates and a snowboard for my birthday.**
2. **Well my friend you can't always have what you want when you want it.**
3. **No but I can always hope!**
4. **My friends and I skate all year long and snowboard during the winter.**
5. **I used to like skateboarding but now I prefer snowboarding and in-line skating.**
6. **What sports games or hobbies do you enjoy most Jody?**
7. **I learned to ski last year and now I'm taking ice-skating lessons.**
8. **Skiing ice skating and skateboarding are all fun things to do.**

Review the four rules above for using commas. Then write an original sentence for each rule. Begin and end each sentence correctly. Remember to check your spelling.

9. ______________________________

10. ______________________________

11. ______________________________

12. ______________________________

**Writers use commas for other reasons. As you read a newspaper, an article in your favorite magazine, a letter, or a book, look for examples of commas in sentences and jot them down on a sheet of paper. Then see if you can figure out the rules.**

# Fractions Are a Breeze

Sail into fractions by renaming each fraction below in lowest terms.

If the fraction is equal to 1/2 or 3/4, shade the box blue.

If the fraction is equal to 1/4, shade the box yellow.

If the fraction is equal to 1/3, shade the box green.

If the boxes are coloured correctly, a picture will appear.

| | | | | | | |
|---|---|---|---|---|---|---|
| $\frac{3}{6}$ | $\frac{2}{8}$ | $\frac{21}{42}$ | $\frac{75}{150}$ | $\frac{31}{62}$ | $\frac{11}{22}$ | $\frac{7}{14}$ |
| $\frac{50}{100}$ | $\frac{9}{36}$ | $\frac{11}{44}$ | $\frac{32}{64}$ | $\frac{30}{60}$ | $\frac{6}{12}$ | $\frac{60}{120}$ |
| $\frac{4}{8}$ | $\frac{7}{28}$ | $\frac{16}{64}$ | $\frac{3}{12}$ | $\frac{8}{16}$ | $\frac{40}{80}$ | $\frac{12}{16}$ |
| $\frac{9}{18}$ | $\frac{25}{100}$ | $\frac{6}{24}$ | $\frac{8}{32}$ | $\frac{19}{76}$ | $\frac{48}{64}$ | $\frac{5}{10}$ |
| $\frac{10}{20}$ | $\frac{17}{68}$ | $\frac{12}{48}$ | $\frac{13}{52}$ | $\frac{20}{80}$ | $\frac{25}{100}$ | $\frac{14}{28}$ |
| $\frac{35}{70}$ | $\frac{8}{32}$ | $\frac{10}{40}$ | $\frac{15}{60}$ | $\frac{40}{160}$ | $\frac{14}{56}$ | $\frac{5}{20}$ |
| $\frac{21}{28}$ | $\frac{12}{24}$ | $\frac{40}{80}$ | $\frac{15}{30}$ | $\frac{33}{66}$ | $\frac{15}{20}$ | $\frac{75}{100}$ |
| $\frac{2}{6}$ / $\frac{5}{10}$ | $\frac{12}{36}$ | $\frac{9}{27}$ | $\frac{30}{90}$ | $\frac{20}{60}$ | $\frac{11}{33}$ | $\frac{6}{18}$ / $\frac{2}{4}$ |
| $\frac{18}{24}$ | $\frac{5}{15}$ / $\frac{9}{12}$ | $\frac{15}{45}$ | $\frac{8}{24}$ | $\frac{10}{30}$ | $\frac{3}{9}$ / $\frac{6}{8}$ | $\frac{30}{40}$ |

# Moonwalkers on City Streets

Do you need some exercise? Do you want to see some city sights? Perhaps you want to assert your rights as a pedestrian in a city designed for cars. Then you might want to make your own group, inspired by a group called Moonwalkers in Pennsylvania, the US. The Moonwalkers meet once a week at night. Then they stride through their city, up hills, down streets, over bridges, and along canals. What are some other reasons that people enjoy moonwalking? They get to meet other members of their community, and they enjoy being out at night.

**Find five causes and one effect in the passage. Write them on the map.**

**Causes** → **Effect**

MORE! Make a list of five synonyms for the word *walk*. Use each word in a sentence.

# What's Hoppin'?

**You Answer It!**

1. Look at the graph below. Starting at square X, Judy hopped 4 squares up and 3 squares to the right. In which square did she land?

___________________________

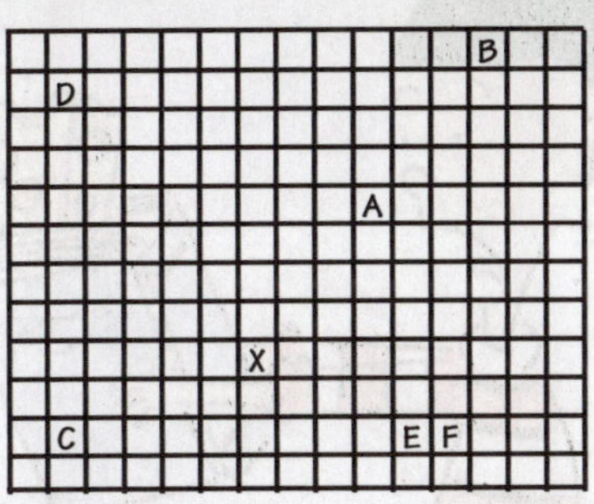


**NOTE: Judy and Rudy can hop in vertical and horizontal directions only.**

2. Rudy is in square X. Which are the 2 shortest paths he can take to get to square E?

___________________________

___________________________

3. Judy is in square A. Which are the 2 shortest paths she can take to get to square E?

___________________________

___________________________

4. Find the 2 shortest paths to get from square X to square D.

___________________________

___________________________

5. Find 3 paths to get from square D to square E. Does each path contain the same total number of squares?

___________________________

___________________________

6. Starting at square X, Rudy hopped 6 squares up and 5 squares to the left. How many squares is he from square D?

___________________________

___________________________

# Stories Behind Inventions That Changed the World
## (That May or May Not Be True)

Find and mark the 11 spelling errors.

### The Jacket Zipper

The first zipper, the Model 100-A, was made of solid wood and weyed over 8 kilogrram. Over time, the size decreased. Metal replased wood. A solid gold zipper weighed in at only 120 grammes. Unfortunatelly, it cost over $1,500 (approx ₹100,000). Finally, the Model 100-Z came out. It was a lot like the zipper of today—except two people were required to zip it up.

### The Bookmark

Ted E. Bear, in a 1997 interview, discloseed, "I kept loosing my place in the book I was reading. I tried putting a peece of cheese in there, but it was greasy. I tried a giant rock. It was too heavy and awkward. I tried a $100 bill (Rs 6500 approx). It worked well, but that was all the money I had! Finally, I tried a small slip of paper. At last, the bookmark was born!

### The Cereal Spoon

First, people tried to eat cereal with their hands. What a mess! There was milk driping from everyone's elbows. Next, a garden shovel was tried. Too big! It was replaced with a fork. The size was good, but it leaked. Finally, someone pulled out a spoon. There was little chance after so many faillurs that it would work. But it was perfect!

# Beekeeping Basics

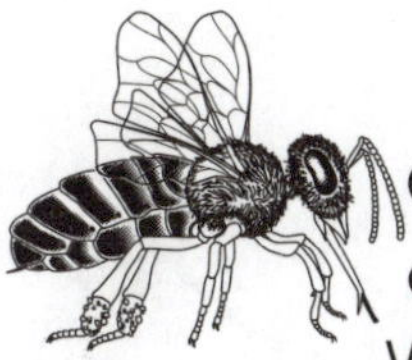

Open a jar of golden honey. Spread some on a slice of toast. Take a bite and enjoy its special sweetness. There's nothing else quite like it!

Where does honey come from? Bees make it, right? But wait! Bees are insects. They don't set up little factories for making honey and putting it in jars, do they? What's the real story behind the honey we eat?

Since ancient times, people have known that bees make a delicious, sweet food. To get it, people would search for a hive of wild bees and steal the honey. Then some people figured out that they could get honey more easily if they made hives for bees to live in. They became beekeepers.

The first hives were probably hollow logs or clay pots turned on their sides. Later, in about 1500, farmers in Europe began building straw beehives that looked like baskets turned upside down. Farmers from Europe brought honeybees with them to America in the 1600s.

Around 1850, an American beekeeper invented a better kind of hive called the hanging movable-frame beehive. It looks like a stack of boxes. Inside are wooden frames where bees build wax honeycombs for storing their honey. This is the kind of hive that most beekeepers use today.

The amazing thing about a beehive is how much it actually is like a little factory for making honey. Each hive is home to a colony of as many as 60,000 bees. A colony has one queen that lays eggs. Other bees have different jobs, such as building the honeycomb, keeping it clean, feeding the young, or making honey. Some bees are guards that protect the hive. If a guard thinks you are a danger to the colony, it will sting you.

Honey is made from nectar, a sweet liquid inside flowers. A bee sucks nectar from a flower and then brings it back to the hive. A wax-making bee places the nectar in a honey cell. Other bees add more and more nectar to the honey cell. The nectar is mostly water when it is first brought to the hive. "House bees" fan their wings over the cell to remove the water. As the water evaporates, the nectar changes into honey. When the honey in a cell is ready, the bees cover it with a wax cap.

Beekeepers give the bees several months to fill the honeycombs in a hive. Bees must gather nectar from more than a million flowers to make just one pound of honey! When the honey is ready to harvest, beekeepers wear special clothes that cover their bodies completely. Otherwise, they would surely be stung many times as they pull frames filled with honey from the hive.

Using special tools, beekeepers can extract the honey without breaking the honeycomb. They do this so that the bees will not need to rebuild the honeycomb. When the beekeeper puts the frames back into the hive, the bees will start filling them with honey again.

No bee can make honey alone. It takes a large team of very hard workers to get the job done. We could learn a lot from these little creatures about working together and getting things done.

1. **Beekeepers extract honey without breaking the honeycomb. What does extract mean?**

   Ⓐ take out  Ⓒ make
   Ⓑ fill up  Ⓓ eat

2. **How is a beehive like a factory?**

   ________________________________________
   ________________________________________
   ________________________________________

3. **List four steps in the making of honey.**

   ________________________________________
   ________________________________________
   ________________________________________
   ________________________________________

4. **Which sentence best states the main idea of this article?**

   Ⓕ Be careful around honeybees—they sting!
   Ⓖ An American invented the best kind of beehive.
   Ⓗ Honeybees are useful and interesting creatures.
   Ⓙ Beekeepers have been around for a long time.

# Identifying Relationships

Write the phrase from the box that tells how the first two words are related.
Then write the correct word to complete the analogy.

| Relationship: | Same Class | Part/Whole | Synonyms |
|---|---|---|---|
| | Antonyms | Homophones | |

1. weight : wait :: gilt : _____ Relationship _______________
   Ⓐ wave Ⓑ guilt Ⓒ gill

2. work : play :: deep : _____ Relationship _______________
   Ⓐ shallow Ⓑ dive Ⓒ job

3. elm : pine :: bee : _____ Relationship _______________
   Ⓐ birch Ⓑ honey Ⓒ beetle

4. seam : seem :: I : _____ Relationship _______________
   Ⓐ me Ⓑ eye Ⓒ you

5. kernel : corn :: seed : _____ Relationship _______________
   Ⓐ soil Ⓑ water Ⓒ watermelon

6. forest : woods :: field : _____ Relationship _______________
   Ⓐ meadow Ⓑ flower Ⓒ farmer

7. leave : arrive :: asked : _____ Relationship _______________
   Ⓐ go Ⓑ told Ⓒ inquired

8. wheel : we'll :: hall : _____ Relationship _______________
   Ⓐ help Ⓑ hill Ⓒ haul

**Explain to someone in your family how you chose each answer.**

# Free-Throw Percentage

Hoops, Dunk'n, and Shooter are on the court again! How do their numbers add up? Follow the steps below to make sense of their percents.

1. Hoops took 10 free throws and made 4. What percentage did he make?

   4/10 = ______/100 = ______%

2. Dunk'n took 4 free throws and made 3.
   a. What fraction did he make? ________ = __________/100
   b. What fractions did he miss? _________ = __________/100
   c. What percent did he make? ____________%
   d. What percent did he miss? ___________%

3. Shooter took 20 free throws and made 13.
   a. What fraction did he make? ______
   b. What fraction did he miss? ________
   c. What percent did he make? ______
   d. What percent did he miss? _______

## All-Star Maths!

4. Hoops makes 60 per cent of the free throws he takes.
   a. In lowest terms, what fraction of free throws did he make? _______
   b. If he took 10 free throws, how many should he make? ______
   c. If he took 15 free throws, how many should he make? ______
   d. If he took 200 free throws, how many should he make? ______

**Remember!**

Percents are fractions of 100.
For example: 25/100 = 25%
Or 3/25 = 12/100 = 12%

THIS CERTIFIES THAT

_______________________________

IS NOW READY

FOR GRADE ____

# CONGRATULATIONS!

I'm proud of you! _______________________